Essential Skills for Math Success:

Strategies for Mathematical Problem Solving and Test Taking

by Howard I. Berrent, Ph.D. and Edward R. Nasello

Level G

RALLY! EDUCATION, LLC

Glen Head, New York

RALLY!
EDUCATION

We're all about student success!

ISBN 1-58380-860-4

Published 2005
Printed in the U.S.A.

Cover Designer: Jean-Paul Vest
Book Designer/Production: Jan Jarvis
Editor: Christina Quinlan

RALLY! EDUCATION
22 Railroad Avenue
Glen Head, NY 11545
tel 888·99·RALLY
fax 516·671·7900
www.RALLYEDUCATION.com

Essential Skills for Math Success
Strategies for Mathematical Problem Solving and Test Taking

Table of Contents

Introduction

Welcome to *Essential Skills for Math Success: Strategies for Mathematical Problem Solving and Test Taking*. To be successful in math, you must become a good problem solver. This book will teach you problem-solving skills and show you how to apply them to different types of math problems.

Essential Skills for Math Success is made up of two parts:

Part A will teach you how to follow a plan, use problem-solving strategies, and solve different types of math problems. Part A has three sections.

Part B will test your ability to use different strategies to solve the types of math problems learned in Part A.

The 5-Step Problem-Solving Plan

Good problem solvers always follow a plan. A plan guides you by outlining a series of steps to follow. The plan discussed in this book consists of five steps:

Step 1   DECIDE what you are being asked to do.
Step 2   FIND what you need to know.
Step 3   CHOOSE a strategy for solving the problem.
Step 4   SOLVE the problem.
Step 5   CHECK your answer.

The 10 Problem-Solving Strategies

A strategy is a method or way of doing something. Sometimes more than one strategy can be used to solve a problem. Knowing how to choose the best strategy for solving a problem will make you successful in math. This book will show you how to use the following 10 strategies to solve math problems:

Strategy 1   Draw a Picture or Diagram
Strategy 2   Organize—Make a Chart or List, Graph, Sort Data
Strategy 3   Work Backwards
Strategy 4   Use Manipulatives or Act Out
Strategy 5   Compute—Write a Number Sentence, Use Ratio or Proportion
Strategy 6   Use a Formula or Rule
Strategy 7   Guess and Check
Strategy 8   Make It Simpler
Strategy 9   Make Estimates
Strategy 10   Look for a Pattern

The 7 Math Strands

Math is organized by seven strands. The exercises in this book will teach you to solve problems related to each of these 7 math strands:

Strand 1   Numbers & Operations
Strand 2   Patterns & Functions
Strand 3   Algebra
Strand 4   Geometry
Strand 5   Measurement
Strand 6   Data Analysis
Strand 7   Probability/Uncertainty

First we will model what we teach. Then we will guide you as you solve problems in each strand. Finally we will provide you with Independent Study. This you will do on your own.

When you finish *Essential Skills for Math Success* you will be a better problem solver and a better test taker.

PART A

Strategies and Strands— *One-by-One*

Each problem-solving strategy and math strand is taught one-by-one in this part. Part A is divided into three sections.

Section 1: The 5-Step Problem-Solving Plan
In this section, you will learn to follow a plan whenever you solve a math problem. We will show you each step in the plan. Then you will use the plan on your own.

Section 2: The 10 Problem-Solving Strategies One-by-One
This section will teach you ten problem-solving strategies. These strategies are tools that will help you solve multiple-choice, short-response, or extended-response questions. You will see examples of each type of question throughout this book.

First we will show you how to use each strategy with the 5-Step Problem-Solving Plan. You will solve one problem using the strategy on your own before moving on to the next strategy.

Section 3: The 7 Math Strands One-by-One
In this section, you will learn about the 7 Math Strands. For each strand there are three parts: Modeled Instruction, Guided Instruction, and Independent Study.

In **Modeled Instruction**, we will show you a problem related to each strand. We will show you how to follow a plan and choose a good strategy for solving the problem.

In **Guided Instruction**, we will provide *Hints* for you on a possible strategy you can use to solve the problem. Sometimes more than one strategy can be used to solve problems related to a particular strand.

In **Independent Study**, you will solve four problems on your own. After you solve each problem, you will be asked which strategy you chose. You will answer multiple-choice, short-response, and extended-response questions.

Section 1: The 5-Step Problem-Solving Plan

Section 2: The 10 Problem-Solving Strategies One-by-One

Section 3: The 7 Math Strands One-by-One

A Section 1: The 5-Step Problem-Solving Plan

Modeled Instruction

When solving math problems, you need to follow a plan. This helps you to organize information and choose a strategy to solve the problem. The example below shows how to follow the 5-Step Problem-Solving Plan. Read the math problem and follow each step of the plan.

The 5-Step Problem-Solving Plan

Step 1 DECIDE → Step 2 FIND → Step 3 CHOOSE → Step 4 SOLVE → Step 5 CHECK

Tanisha has two containers. There are $24\frac{1}{2}$ ounces of juice in one of the containers and $33\frac{1}{4}$ ounces in the other. Using all of the juice in both containers, Tanisha pours an equal amount of juice into 11 cups. There are 6 blue cups and 5 red cups. How much juice does she pour into each cup?

(A) 8 ounces

(B) $6\frac{1}{2}$ ounces

(C) 6 ounces

(D) $5\frac{1}{4}$ ounces

Step 1: DECIDE what you are being asked to do.

The problem tells you how much juice is in two separate containers and how many cups of juice Tanisha must pour. You must calculate how much juice she pours into each cup.

Step 2: FIND what you need to know.

You can find the following information in the problem:

- There are $24\frac{1}{2}$ ounces of juice in one container.

- There are $33\frac{1}{4}$ ounces of juice in another container.

- Tanisha uses all of the juice in both containers to pour an equal amount of juice into 11 cups.

PART A: Strategies and Strands—One-by-One

Step 3: CHOOSE a strategy for solving the problem.

There is often more than one way to solve a math problem. In this book, you will learn how to use several problem-solving strategies. Try writing a number sentence to solve word problems like this one. Use the information given in the problem to write the number sentence.

Step 4: SOLVE the problem.

First, write a number sentence to find the total ounces of juice in the two containers.

$$24\frac{1}{2} + 33\frac{1}{4} = \text{total ounces of juice in both containers}$$

Rewrite the number sentence using fractions that have a common denominator and solve.

$$24\frac{1}{2} + 33\frac{1}{4} = 57\frac{3}{4} \text{ ounces}$$

Now that you know the total amount of juice in the two containers, write another number sentence to find how much juice Tanisha pours into each cup.

$$57\frac{3}{4} \div 11 = \text{ounces of juice that are poured into each cup}$$

In order to solve this number sentence, you must convert 11 and the mixed number $57\frac{3}{4}$ into fractions.

$$\frac{231}{4} \div \frac{11}{1} = \underline{\hspace{2cm}}$$

When dividing fractions, remember to multiply by the reciprocal of the divisor.

$$\frac{231}{4} \times \frac{11}{1} = \frac{231}{44}$$

Now change the fraction into a mixed number in order to get the answer to this problem.

$$\frac{231}{44} = 5\frac{11}{44} = 5\frac{1}{4}$$

Since Tanisha must pour $5\frac{1}{4}$ ounces of juice into each cup, the correct answer to the problem is choice "D."

Step 5: CHECK your answer.

To check your answer, work backwards. Multiply the number of ounces in each cup by the total number of cups.

$$5\frac{1}{4} \times 11 = 57$$

The product should equal the total ounces of juice in the two containers.

On Your Own

Follow the 5-Step Problem-Solving Plan to answer the next two questions on your own.

> **The table to the right shows how many miles Grant and Corinne jogged each day last week.**
>
> **Which decimal represents the difference between the total miles Grant and Corinne each jogged for the entire week?**
>
> | Day of Week | Distance Grant Jogged (in miles) | Distance Corinne Jogged (in miles) |
> |---|---|---|
> | Monday | 2.20 | 2.25 |
> | Tuesday | 2.75 | 1.90 |
> | Wednesday | 1.80 | 2.75 |
> | Thursday | 3.00 | 2.50 |
> | Friday | 2.50 | 3.00 |
>
> Ⓐ .15   Ⓑ .20   Ⓒ .35   Ⓓ .50

 DECIDE what you are being asked to do.

State what the problem is asking you to do.

 SOLVE the problem.

Show your work for solving this problem.

FIND what you need to know.

List key facts from the problem. Remember, some problems will give extra information that you do not need to know.

CHECK your answer.

Show or explain how you know that your answer makes sense.

 CHOOSE a strategy for solving the problem.

Name the strategy you choose to solve this problem.

Peter buys 1 notebook and 6 pens. He gives the cashier $10.00 and receives $3.15 in change. A notebook costs $2.35. How much does one pen cost if Peter paid the same amount of money for each pen?

Answer: _____

 DECIDE what you are being asked to do.

State what the problem is asking you to do.

 FIND what you need to know.

List key facts from the problem.

 CHOOSE a strategy for solving the problem.

Name the strategy you choose to solve this problem.

 SOLVE the problem.

Show your work for solving this problem.

 CHECK your answer.

Show or explain how you know that your answer makes sense.

Section 2: The 10 Problem-Solving Strategies One-by-One

This section will teach you ten problem-solving strategies. These strategies are tools that will help you solve multiple-choice, short-response, or extended-response questions. You will see examples of each type of question throughout this book.

First we will show you how to use each strategy with the 5-Step Problem-Solving Plan. You will solve one problem using the strategy on your own before moving on to the next strategy.

The 10 Problem-Solving Strategies

Strategy 1	Draw a Picture or Diagram
Strategy 2	Organize—Make a Chart or List, Graph, Sort Data
Strategy 3	Work Backwards
Strategy 4	Use Manipulatives or Act Out
Strategy 5	Compute—Write a Number Sentence, Use Ratio or Proportion
Strategy 6	Use a Formula or Rule
Strategy 7	Guess and Check
Strategy 8	Make It Simpler
Strategy 9	Make Estimates
Strategy 10	Look for a Pattern

As you use each strategy, don't forget to follow the 5-Step Problem-Solving Plan. It will help you choose the best strategy for solving a problem.

Modeled Instruction

Now you will learn how to solve a math problem by drawing a picture. Read the problem below. The plan that follows will explain how to use this strategy.

> **A right triangle is drawn on a coordinate grid. One vertex is located at the coordinates (2,4) and another vertex at the coordinates (8,8). At which coordinates could the last vertex of the triangle be located?**
>
> Ⓐ   (3,8)   Ⓒ   (6,4)
>
> Ⓑ   (5,8)   Ⓓ   (8,4)

DECIDE what you are being asked to do.

You must use the information given in the problem to find the coordinates of the remaining vertex of the right triangle.

FIND what you need to know.

You can use the coordinates of the two known vertices to find the location of the remaining vertex. The two known vertices are located at (2,4) and (8,8). Consider what a right triangle looks like. Two of the sides in a right triangle must intersect to form a 90° angle.

CHOOSE a strategy for solving the problem.

Problems that involve coordinate grids and shapes can often be solved using the strategy called *Draw a Picture or Diagram*. A picture or diagram can help you see the answer to a problem.

SOLVE the problem.

First plot the two known vertices on a coordinate grid.

Look at the two vertices you have plotted on the grid. Plot additional vertices at any coordinates on the grid that will allow you to form a right triangle.

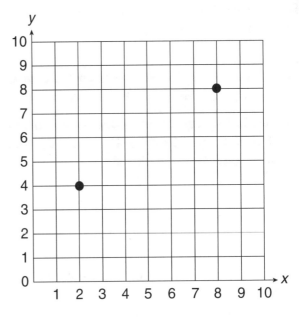

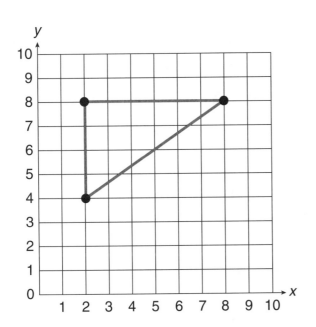
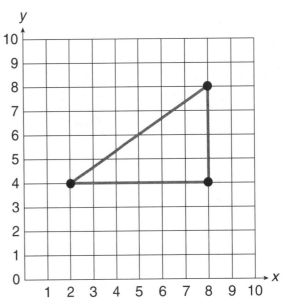

Now you can see that coordinates (2,8) and (8,4) are the only possible coordinates that will complete the right triangle. Only one of these coordinates is given as an answer choice. The correct answer to the problem is choice "D."

CHECK your answer.

One way to check your answer is to plot the coordinates from each of the answer choices along with the coordinates given in the problem. Look to see which set of vertices forms a right triangle.

On Your Own

Directions: Solve the problem below using the *Draw a Picture or Diagram* strategy. Remember to follow the 5-Step Problem-Solving Plan.

Points *A*, *B*, and *C* are plotted on a grid at the coordinates indicated in the table to the right.

∠*ABC* is formed by drawing lines to connect Point *A* to Point *B*, and Point *B* to Point *C*. What type of angle is formed?

Point	Coordinates
A	(2,7)
B	(5,5)
C	(9,5)

Ⓐ obtuse   Ⓑ right   Ⓒ acute   Ⓓ straight

 DECIDE what you are being asked to do.

State what the problem is asking you to do.

 FIND what you need to know.
List key facts from the problem.

CHOOSE a strategy for solving the problem.
Name the strategy you choose to solve this problem.

 SOLVE the problem.

Show your work for solving this problem.

 CHECK your answer.
Show or explain how you know that your answer makes sense.

Strategy 2: Organize—Make a Chart or List, Graph, Sort Data

Modeled Instruction

Now you will learn how to solve a math problem by making a chart or list, making a graph, or sorting data. Read the problem below. The plan that follows will explain how to use this strategy.

Mr. Roberts must choose a shirt and a tie to wear to work. He has a blue shirt, a white shirt, and a gray shirt. He also has a black tie, a blue tie, and a red tie. How many different shirt and tie combinations does Mr. Roberts have to choose from?

Answer:_____

DECIDE what you are being asked to do.

You must determine how many different color combinations can be made using the shirts and ties that Mr. Roberts has.

FIND what you need to know.

The problem states that Mr. Roberts has one blue shirt, one white shirt, and one gray shirt. It also states that he has one black tie, one blue tie, and one red tie.

CHOOSE a strategy for solving the problem.

There are several shirt and tie combinations that Mr. Roberts can create. The best way to identify all of the possible combinations is to use the strategy called *Organize—Make a Chart or List, Graph, Sort Data.*

SOLVE the problem.

Create separate lists to show all of the different color ties that can go with each different color shirt.

blue shirt, black tie	white shirt, black tie	gray shirt, black tie
blue shirt, blue tie	white shirt, blue tie	gray shirt, blue tie
blue shirt, red tie	white shirt, red tie	gray shirt, red tie

Mr. Roberts can create nine different shirt and tie combinations.

CHECK your answer.

Make sure that you have listed all of the possible combinations of shirts and ties. Check that each combination is listed only once.

On Your Own

Directions: Solve the problem below using the *Organize—Make a Chart or List, Graph, Sort Data* strategy. Remember to follow the 5-Step Problem-Solving Plan.

The spinner to the right is used to play a game.

On each turn, a player must spin the arrow a total of three times. The player records the result of each spin on a piece of paper. How many outcomes are possible when the arrow is spun three times?

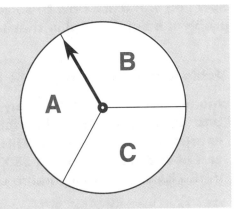

Answer:_____

 DECIDE what you are being asked to do.

State what the problem is asking you to do.

 FIND what you need to know.

List key facts from the problem.

 CHOOSE a strategy for solving the problem.

Name the strategy you choose to solve this problem.

 SOLVE the problem.

Show your work for solving this problem.

 CHECK your answer.

Show or explain how you know that your answer makes sense.

Modeled Instruction

Now you will learn how to solve a math problem by working backwards. Read the problem below. The plan that follows will explain how to use this strategy.

Fabio had some money in the bank at the beginning of the year. He took $\frac{1}{4}$ of his money out of the bank to buy a gift for his mother. Then he deposited $50.00 back into his account. For keeping money in the bank for the entire year, Fabio earned $11.36 in interest. This money was also added to his bank account. At the end of the year Fabio had $802.39 in the bank. How much money did Fabio have in the bank at the beginning of the year?

Ⓐ $863.75   Ⓑ $898.36   Ⓒ $934.25   Ⓓ $988.04

DECIDE what you are being asked to do.

You must find how much money Fabio had in the bank at the beginning of the year.

FIND what you need to know.

You can find the following information in the problem:

- Fabio took $\frac{1}{4}$ of his money out of the bank to buy a gift for his mother.

- He deposited $50.00 back into his bank account.

- He earned $11.36 in interest.

- At the end of the year Fabio had $802.39 in his bank account.

CHOOSE a strategy for solving the problem.

The problem tells you how much money Fabio had in the bank at the end of the year. It does not tell you how much money Fabio had in the bank at the beginning of the year. A good strategy for solving this type of math problem is to *Work Backwards*.

SOLVE the problem.

Start with how much money Fabio had in his bank account at the end of the year:

$802.39

Find how much money he had before the interest that he earned was added to his account:

$802.39 − $11.36 = $791.03

Find how much money he had before adding $50.00 to his account:

$791.03 − $50 = $741.03

Now you know that Fabio had $741.03 before using $\frac{1}{4}$ of his money to buy his mother a gift. Therefore, $741.03 is equal to $\frac{3}{4}$ of the money Fabio had in the bank at the beginning of the year.

$$1 - \frac{1}{4} = \underline{} \longrightarrow \frac{4}{4} - \frac{1}{4} = \frac{3}{4}$$

Set up a ratio, using x to represent the amount of money Fabio had in the bank at the beginning of the year. Solve for x to find how much money was in Fabio's bank account before he used $\frac{1}{4}$ of it to buy his mother a gift. This is the amount of money Fabio had in the bank at the beginning of the year.

$$\frac{\$741.03}{x} = \frac{3}{4} \longrightarrow 3x = 4 \times \$741.03 \longrightarrow 3x = \$2,964.12$$

$$x = \$2,964.12 \div 3 \longrightarrow x = \$988.04$$

Since you have calculated that Fabio had $988.04 in the bank at the beginning of the year, the correct answer is choice "D."

CHECK your answer.

You now know how much money Fabio had in the bank at the beginning of the year. Read the problem again and check to see that your answer makes sense.

Amount of money in Fabio's bank account at the beginning of the year:

$988.04

Fabio used $\frac{1}{4}$ of the money to buy a gift for his mother:

$988.04 − ($988.04 × .25) $\longrightarrow$ $988.04 − $247.01 = $741.03

Fabio deposited $50.00 back into his bank account:

$741.03 + $50.00 = $791.03

Fabio earned $11.36 in interest:

$791.03 + $11.36 = $802.39

Amount of money in Fabio's bank account at the end of the year:

$802.39

On Your Own

Directions: Solve the problem below using the *Work Backwards* strategy. Remember to follow the 5-Step Problem-Solving Plan.

Miss Dowd used a container of apple juice to fill 5 large cups and 4 small cups. She poured 7.75 ounces of apple juice into each large cup. Then she poured 4.50 ounces into each small cup. When Miss Dowd finished filling all of the cups there were 6.25 ounces of apple juice left in the container. How much apple juice was in the container to begin with?

(A) 62.75 ounces   (B) 63.00 ounces   (C) 63.25 ounces   (D) 64.00 ounces

 DECIDE what you are being asked to do.

State what the problem is asking you to do.

 FIND what you need to know.

List key facts from the problem.

 CHOOSE a strategy for solving the problem.

Name the strategy you choose to solve this problem.

 SOLVE the problem.

Show your work for solving this problem.

 CHECK your answer.

Show or explain how you know that your answer makes sense.

Strategy 4: Use Manipulatives or Act Out

Modeled Instruction

Now you will learn how to solve a math problem by using manipulatives or acting it out. Read the problem below. The plan that follows will explain how to use this strategy.

> Aswad, Cheng, Bernard, Carlotta, and Matthew are on the school track team. During one race, Bernard crossed the finish line first and Carlotta finished last. Each of the other students crossed the finish line at different times. List all of the different possible outcomes for the order in which the five students crossed the finish line.
>
> Answer:

 DECIDE what you are being asked to do.

You must determine all of the different possible outcomes for the order in which the five students crossed the finish line.

 FIND what you need to know.

You know that Bernard crossed the finish line first and Carlotta crossed the finish line last. You do not know the order in which the other three students crossed the finish line. There are several possibilities. You must list them all.

 CHOOSE a strategy for solving the problem.

Problems that involve arranging the order of objects or people can often be solved using a strategy called *Use Manipulatives or Act Out*. Manipulatives are objects used to act out math problems. Use manipulatives to represent the students in this problem.

SOLVE the problem.

Write the names of each student on separate pieces of paper. Then arrange the names to show the order in which the students could have crossed the finish line. Remember, you already know that Bernard crossed the finish line first and Carlotta finished last. Write down the result.

Rearrange the pieces of paper, keeping Bernard's name first and Carlotta's last.

Write down the result. Keep repeating these steps until you have listed all of the possible outcomes.

Using the manipulatives you created, you can see that each of the following outcomes is also possible:

CHECK your answer.

Carefully check the order of the student in each outcome you listed. Each possible outcome should appear only once. Do not leave out any possible outcomes.

On Your Own

Directions: Solve the problem below using the *Use Manipulatives or Act Out* strategy. Remember to follow the 5-Step Problem-Solving Plan.

Two number cubes are used to play a game. The sides of each cube are numbered from 1 to 6. On his or her turn, a player must roll both cubes at the same time. The sum of the numbers that are face up on each cube determines how many spaces the player can move on the game board. List all of the possible number combinations that a player can roll to move nine spaces on the game board.

Answer:

 step 1 DECIDE what you are being asked to do.

State what the problem is asking you to do.

 step 2 FIND what you need to know.

List key facts from the problem.

CHOOSE a strategy for solving the problem.

Name the strategy you choose to solve this problem.

 SOLVE the problem.

Show your work for solving this problem.

 CHECK your answer.

Show or explain how you know that your answer makes sense.

Strategy 5: Compute—Write a Number Sentence, Use Ratio or Proportion

Modeled Instruction

Now you will learn how to solve a math problem by writing a number sentence or using ratio or proportion. Read the problem below. The plan that follows will explain how to use this strategy.

Pearl uses some glue and some paper to make a craft. To make three crafts she uses 5.25 ounces of glue and six sheets of paper. Pearl wants to make fifty crafts. How much glue will she need if she uses the same amount to make each craft?

Ⓐ   262.5 ounces   Ⓑ   150.5 ounces   Ⓒ   87.5 ounces   Ⓓ   31.5 ounces

---

DECIDE what you are being asked to do.

You must find how much glue Pearl needs to make fifty crafts.

FIND what you need to know.

You know that Pearl uses 5.25 ounces of glue for every three crafts that she makes. You also know that Pearl would like to make fifty crafts and that she will use the same amount of glue to make each one.

You do NOT need to know that Pearl used six sheets of paper to make three crafts. This is extra information that does not help you solve the problem.

CHOOSE a strategy for solving the problem.

Since you know how many ounces of glue Pearl uses for every three crafts, you can calculate how many ounces of glue she needs to make fifty crafts by using a strategy called *Compute—Write a Number Sentence, Use Ratio or Proportion*.

SOLVE the problem.

First, create a ratio that shows how many ounces of glue are used to make three crafts.

$$\frac{\text{ounces of glue}}{\text{number of crafts}} \longrightarrow \frac{5.25}{3}$$

Next, create another ratio that shows how many ounces of glue are needed to make fifty crafts. Since you do not yet know how many ounces of glue are needed, use the letter x to represent this number.

$$\frac{\text{ounces of glue}}{\text{number of crafts}} \longrightarrow \frac{x}{50}$$

Now use the ratios you have created to set up a proportion. Then solve for x.

$$\frac{5.25}{3} = \frac{x}{50}$$

To solve for x you must cross multiply and then divide.

$3x = 5.25 \cdot 50$

$3x = 262.5$

$x = 262.5 \div 3$

$x = 87.5$

Based on these calculations, choice "C" is the correct answer.

CHECK your answer.

One way to check your answer is to determine how many ounces of glue are needed to make one craft, and then multiply by 50.

ounces of glue needed to make 1 craft:	$5.25 \div 3 = 1.75$
ounces of glue needed to make 50 crafts:	$1.75 \cdot 50 = 87.5$

On Your Own

Directions: Solve the problem below using the *Compute—Write a Number Sentence, Use Ratio or Proportion* strategy. Remember to follow the 5-Step Problem-Solving Plan.

> **Javier follows a recipe to make a fruit salad. For every 3 oranges that he uses he must add 12 grapes and 9 mangoes. How many grapes will be in the salad if there are 15 mangoes?**
>
> Ⓐ 18   Ⓑ 20   Ⓒ 24   Ⓓ 36

 DECIDE what you are being asked to do.

State what the problem is asking you to do.

 SOLVE the problem.

Show your work for solving this problem.

 FIND what you need to know.

List key facts from the problem.

 CHECK your answer.

Show or explain how you know that your answer makes sense.

 CHOOSE a strategy for solving the problem.

Name the strategy you choose to solve this problem.

Modeled Instruction

Now you will learn how to solve a math problem by using a formula or rule. Read the problem below. The plan that follows will explain how to use this strategy.

Selma purchased carpet and tiles to cover her bedroom floor. Her room is rectangular in shape and so is the carpet. The bedroom floor measures 7.25 meters in length and 4.50 meters in width. The carpet measures 4.50 meters in length and 2.75 meters in width. Selma used the tiles to cover the portion of her bedroom floor not covered by the carpet. How big is the area of Selma's bedroom floor that is covered by tiles, in square meters?

Answer:_____

DECIDE what you are being asked to do.

You must find the area of the floor in Selma's bedroom that is covered by tiles. Area is always measured in square units. In this problem, the area of the floor covered by tiles is measured in square meters.

FIND what you need to know.

You know that Selma's bedroom and the carpet that she purchased are both rectangular in shape. You also know the length and width of each of them.

	Selma's Bedroom	Carpet
Length	7.25 meters	4.50 meters
Width	4.50 meters	2.75 meters

CHOOSE a strategy for solving the problem.

A good strategy for solving this problem is to *Use a Formula or Rule*. Formulas are used to calculate the area of shapes and objects. To solve this problem, use the formula for finding the area of a rectangle.

 SOLVE the problem.

First, calculate the area of Selma's bedroom. The problem states that her bedroom is rectangular in shape. The formula for calculating the area of a rectangle is $A = lw$.

Each letter in the formula represents a different measurement.

A = area

l = length

w = width

Replace the letters in the formula with measurements from the problem and solve for A.

$A = 7.25 \times 4.50$

$A = 32.625$ square meters

Next, calculate the area of the floor that is covered by carpet. The carpet is also rectangular in shape.

$A = lw$

$A = 4.50 \times 2.75$

$A = 12.375$ square meters

Selma used tiles to cover the portion of the floor not covered by carpet. Use subtraction to find the area of Selma's bedroom floor that is covered by tiles.

$$\begin{array}{ll} 32.625 & \text{total square meters of floor} \\ -\ 12.375 & \text{square meters of floor covered by carpet} \\ \hline 20.250 & \text{square meters of floor covered by tiles} \end{array}$$

The correct answer is 20.25 square meters.

 CHECK your answer.

Make sure that you have used the correct formula for finding the area of a rectangle. Did you replace each letter in the formula with the correct measurement from the problem? Check that you subtracted correctly.

On Your Own

Directions: Solve the problem below using the *Use a Formula or Rule* strategy. Remember to follow the 5-Step Problem-Solving Plan.

A cube-shaped box with the dimensions shown to the right can hold up to 25 pounds of sugar.

How many cubic inches does it take to hold 150 pounds of sugar?

9.5 in.

Answer: _____

 DECIDE what you are being asked to do.

State what the problem is asking you to do.

 FIND what you need to know.

List key facts from the problem.

 CHOOSE a strategy for solving the problem.

Name the strategy you choose to solve this problem.

 SOLVE the problem.

Show your work for solving this problem.

 CHECK your answer.

Show or explain how you know that your answer makes sense.

Modeled Instruction

Now you will learn how to solve a math problem by guessing and checking. Read the problem below. The plan that follows will explain how to use this strategy.

Which of the following number sentences is true if $n = \dfrac{1}{2}$?

Ⓐ $4\dfrac{5}{8} - (1 \div n) = \dfrac{5}{8}$

Ⓒ $(n \div \dfrac{1}{4}) + \dfrac{1}{4} = \dfrac{3}{8}$

Ⓑ $2\dfrac{5}{8} - (\dfrac{1}{2} \div n) = \dfrac{5}{8}$

Ⓓ $(n \div 4) + \dfrac{1}{4} = \dfrac{3}{8}$

DECIDE what you are being asked to do.

You must find the number sentence that will be true if you replace n with $\dfrac{1}{2}$.

FIND what you need to know.

You are given four possible answer choices. You know that n will equal $\dfrac{1}{2}$ for one of the answer choices.

CHOOSE a strategy for solving the problem.

One of the answer choices you are given must be correct. A good strategy for solving this type of problem is to *Guess and Check*. You can find the correct answer by substituting $\dfrac{1}{2}$ for the letter n in each answer choice.

SOLVE the problem.

Replace the letter n in each number sentence with the fraction $\frac{1}{2}$. Ask yourself which number sentence is true and which number sentences are not true.

Choice A:

$$4\frac{5}{8} - (1 \div n) = \frac{5}{8} \quad \longrightarrow \quad 4\frac{5}{8} - (1 \div \frac{1}{2}) = 4\frac{5}{8} - 2 = \frac{5}{8}$$

This number sentence is NOT true.

Choice B:

$$2\frac{5}{8} - (\frac{1}{2} \div n) = \frac{5}{8} \quad \longrightarrow \quad 2\frac{5}{8} - (\frac{1}{2} \div \frac{1}{2}) = 2\frac{5}{8} - 1 = \frac{5}{8}$$

This number sentence is NOT true.

Choice C:

$$(n \div \frac{1}{4}) + \frac{1}{4} = \frac{3}{8} \quad \longrightarrow \quad (\frac{1}{2} \div \frac{1}{4}) + \frac{1}{4} = 2 + \frac{1}{4} = \frac{3}{8}$$

This number sentence is NOT true.

Choice D:

$$(n \div 4) + \frac{1}{4} = \frac{3}{8} \quad \longrightarrow \quad (\frac{1}{2} \div 4) + \frac{1}{4} = \frac{1}{8} + \frac{1}{4} = \frac{1}{8} + \frac{2}{8} = \frac{3}{8}$$

This number sentence is TRUE.

Answer choice "D" is the only number sentence that is true when the value of n is equal to $\frac{1}{2}$.

CHECK your answer.

Check that your answer makes sense. Carefully review your calculations for each answer choice. Make sure that "D" is the best possible answer.

On Your Own

Directions: Solve the problem below using the *Guess and Check* strategy. Remember to follow the 5-Step Problem-Solving Plan.

Which number sentence is true if $x = \frac{1}{3}$ and $y = \frac{7}{9}$?

(A) $y^2 \div x = \frac{1}{27}$ (B) $x^2 \div y = \frac{1}{7}$ (C) $y = x \div \frac{4}{9}$ (D) $x = y \div \frac{7}{27}$

 DECIDE what you are being asked to do.

State what the problem is asking you to do.

 FIND what you need to know.

List key facts from the problem.

 SOLVE the problem.

Show your work for solving this problem.

 CHECK your answer.

Show or explain how you know that your answer makes sense.

CHOOSE a strategy for solving the problem.

Name the strategy you choose to solve this problem.

Modeled Instruction

Now you will learn how to solve a math problem by making the problem simpler. Read the problem below. The plan that follows will explain how to use this strategy.

Mr. Garza's car uses 13 gallons of gasoline to travel 364 miles. The car can travel up to a speed of 75 miles per hour. Mr. Garza is planning a trip that will require him to travel 1,596 miles in his car. How many gallons of gasoline will be used to make this trip?

Answer: _____

Explain the steps you took to get your answer.

---

step 1

DECIDE what you are being asked to do.

You must calculate how much gasoline is needed for Mr. Garza to travel 1,596 miles in his car.

step 2

FIND what you need to know.

You know that Mr. Garza's car uses 13 gallons of gasoline to travel 364 miles. You also know that Mr. Garza needs to travel 1,596 miles.

You do NOT need to know that the car can travel up to a speed of 75 miles per hour. This is extra information that does not help you solve the problem.

CHOOSE a strategy for solving the problem.

This problem would be easier to solve if you determined how many miles the car can travel for every 1 gallon of gasoline that it uses. This problem-solving strategy is called *Make It Simpler*.

SOLVE the problem.

To calculate how many miles the car can travel for every 1 gallon of gasoline that it uses, you must divide.

miles driven ÷ gallons of gasoline used = miles per gallon of gasoline

364 ÷ 13 = 28 miles per gallon

Now that you know how many miles can be driven using 1 gallon of gasoline, you can calculate how many gallons are needed to travel 1,596 miles.

total miles driven ÷ miles per gallon of gasoline = gallons of gasoline needed

1,596 ÷ 28 = _____

You can make this division problem easier to solve by using factorization.

```
        1,596                    28
      /       \                /    \
   4           399          4        7
```

The common factors can then be removed to simplify the division problem as follows:

399 ÷ 7 = 57

These calculations show that Mr. Garza's car will use 57 gallons of gasoline to travel 1,596 miles. For the second part of the question, you must explain the steps you took to solve the problem.

CHECK your answer.

You can check your answer by working backwards. Multiply the number of gallons of gasoline needed to travel 1,596 miles by the number of miles that can be traveled using 1 gallon.

gallons of gasoline × miles per gallon = total number of miles traveled

57 × 28 = 1,596

On Your Own

Directions: Solve the problem below using the *Make It Simpler* strategy. Remember to follow the 5-Step Problem-Solving Plan.

Millie's Bakery makes 234 cookies every 2 hours and Benny's Bakery makes 345 cookies every 3 hours. After 12 hours, how many more cookies will have been made at Millie's Bakery than at Benny's Bakery?

Answer: _____

Explain the steps you took to get your answer.

 step 1 **DECIDE what you are being asked to do.**
State what the problem is asking you to do.

 step 2 **FIND what you need to know.**
List key facts from the problem.

 step 3 **CHOOSE a strategy for solving the problem.**
Name the strategy you choose to solve this problem.

 step 4 **SOLVE the problem.**
Show your work for solving this problem.

step 5 **CHECK your answer.**
Show or explain how you know that your answer makes sense.

Modeled Instruction

Now you will learn how to solve a math problem by making estimates. Read the problem below. The plan that follows will explain how to use this strategy.

Using one hose, Jay can add 3.16 gallons of water to his swimming pool every 15 seconds. When the pool is filled, the water will measure 5 feet deep. How long will it take Jay to add 235.75 gallons of water to his swimming pool?

(A) 12.64 minutes   (B) 18.65 minutes   (C) 27.28 minutes   (D) 37.92 minutes

DECIDE what you are being asked to do.

You must find how long it will take Jay to add 235.75 gallons of water to his swimming pool.

FIND what you need to know.

You know that Jay can add 3.16 gallons of water to the swimming pool every 15 seconds. You also know that he needs to add 235.75 gallons of water to the pool in all.

You do NOT need to know that the water in the pool will measure 5 feet deep. This is extra information that does not help you solve the problem.

CHOOSE a strategy for solving the problem.

A good strategy for solving problems with decimals is to *Make Estimates*. It is easier to make calculations using estimates.

SOLVE the problem.

First, estimate how much water can be added to the swimming pool every 15 seconds.

   3.16 gallons of water can be rounded to 3 gallons

Next, estimate how much water can be added to the swimming pool every minute. Since there are 60 seconds in 1 minute, you must multiply by 4 (15 seconds × 4 = 60 seconds).

   3 gallons of water × 4 = 12 gallons of water per minute

Now estimate how much water Jay must add to the pool in all.

   235.75 total gallons of water can be rounded to 240 gallons

Using the estimates you made, divide to find how long it will take Jay to add all of the water to the swimming pool.

   240 gallons in all ÷ 12 gallons per minute = 20 minutes

Look at the four answer choices. The answer closest to 20 minutes is 18.65. Therefore, choice "B" is the correct answer.

CHECK your answer.

To check your answer, round each answer choice to the nearest ten.

   Choice A: 12.64 minutes can be rounded to 10 minutes

   Choice B: 18.65 minutes can be rounded to 20 minutes

   Choice C: 27.28 minutes can be rounded to 30 minutes

   Choice D: 37.92 minutes can be rounded to 40 minutes

After you have rounded all of the answer choices, ask yourself if your answer makes sense.

On Your Own

Directions: Solve the problem below using the *Make Estimates* strategy. Remember to follow the 5-Step Problem-Solving Plan.

> The combined weight of 6 paper clips is equal to 6.3 grams. The total weight of paper clips contained in one box is equal to 73.5 grams. A total of 423 boxes of paper clips are packed in 1 crate. How many paper clips are inside the crate?
>
> Ⓐ 19,610 Ⓑ 22,110 Ⓒ 29,610 Ⓓ 32,110

 DECIDE what you are being asked to do.

State what the problem is asking you to do.

 FIND what you need to know.

List key facts from the problem.

 SOLVE the problem.

Show your work for solving this problem.

 CHECK your answer.

Show or explain how you know that your answer makes sense.

 CHOOSE a strategy for solving the problem.

Name the strategy you choose to solve this problem.

Modeled Instruction

Now you will learn how to solve a math problem by looking for a pattern. Read the problem below. The plan that follows will explain how to use this strategy.

The table below shows a relationship between the value of x and the value of y.

x	y
3	7
4	14
5	23
6	34
7	47

Write a number sentence that expresses the relationship between x and y.

Answer: _____

DECIDE what you are being asked to do.

You must use the data provided in the table to write a number sentence that expresses the relationship between the value of x and the value of y.

FIND what you need to know.

The chart provides the following information.

When x is equal to 3, y is equal to 7.

When x is equal to 4, y is equal to 14.

When x is equal to 5, y is equal to 23.

When x is equal to 6, y is equal to 34.

When x is equal to 7, y is equal to 47.

CHOOSE a strategy for solving the problem.

Finding a relationship is similar to finding a pattern. To solve this problem, you can use the strategy called *Look for a Pattern*.

SOLVE the problem.

To find the pattern in the table shown in the problem, compare each value of *x* with each value of *y*. Use different mathematical operations to create a number sentence that shows the relationship between and *x* and *y*. You might try several combinations of mathematical operations before you correctly identify this relationship.

Using multiplication and subtraction, you will find the following relationship:

value of *x*	multiplied by itself	subtract 2	value of *y*
3	3×3 or $3^2 = 9$	$9 - 2 = 7$	7
4	4×4 or $4^2 = 16$	$16 - 2 = 14$	14
5	5×5 or $5^2 = 25$	$25 - 2 = 23$	23
6	6×6 or $6^2 = 36$	$36 - 2 = 34$	34
7	7×7 or $7^2 = 49$	$49 - 2 = 47$	47

Now you can write a number sentence that expresses the relationship you have just discovered.

$$x^2 - 2 = y \quad \text{OR} \quad y = x^2 - 2$$

There are other number sentences that can also be used to express this same relationship in a different way.

$$y + 2 = x^2 \quad \text{OR} \quad x^2 = y + 2$$

CHECK your answer.

Check your answer by substituting the values of *x* and *y* from the table into the number sentence you have written.

$x^2 - 2 = y$

$3^2 - 2 = 7 \quad \longrightarrow \quad 9 - 2 = 7 \quad \longrightarrow \quad 7 = 7$

$4^2 - 2 = 14 \quad \longrightarrow \quad 16 - 2 = 14 \quad \longrightarrow \quad 14 = 14$

$5^2 - 2 = 23 \quad \longrightarrow \quad 25 - 2 = 23 \quad \longrightarrow \quad 23 = 23$

$6^2 - 2 = 34 \quad \longrightarrow \quad 36 - 2 = 34 \quad \longrightarrow \quad 34 = 34$

$7^2 - 2 = 47 \quad \longrightarrow \quad 49 - 2 = 47 \quad \longrightarrow \quad 47 = 47$

These calculations show that you have correctly identified the relationship between the value of *x* and the value of *y*.

On Your Own

Directions: Solve the problem below using the *Look for a Pattern* strategy. Remember to follow the 5-Step Problem-Solving Plan.

Derek plays on the school basketball team. The table below shows how many baskets he attempted and how many baskets he made in the first five games of the season.

Write a number sentence that expresses the relationship between the number of baskets Derek attempted and the number of baskets he made in each of the first five games. Use *x* to represent the number of baskets attempted and *y* to represent the number of baskets made.

	Number of Baskets Attempted	Number of Baskets Made
Game 1	18	10
Game 2	16	9
Game 3	22	12
Game 4	12	7
Game 5	20	11

Answer: _____

 DECIDE what you are being asked to do.

State what the problem is asking you to do.

 FIND what you need to know.

List key facts from the problem.

 SOLVE the problem.

Show your work for solving this problem.

 CHECK your answer.

Show or explain how you know that your answer makes sense.

CHOOSE a strategy for solving the problem.

Name the strategy you choose to solve this problem.

Section 3: The 7 Math Strands One-by-One

In this section, you will learn about the 7 Math Strands. For each strand there are three parts: Modeled Instruction, Guided Instruction, and Independent Study.

In **Modeled Instruction**, we will show you a problem related to each strand. We will show you how to follow a plan and choose a good strategy for solving the problem.

In **Guided Instruction**, we will provide *Hints* for you on a possible strategy you can use to solve the problem. Sometimes more than one strategy can be used to solve problems related to a particular strand.

In **Independent Study**, you will solve four problems on your own. After you solve each problem, you will be asked which strategy you chose. You will answer multiple-choice, short-response, and extended-response questions.

The math problems in Section 3 are organized by the 7 Math Strands.

Strand 1:   Numbers & Operations

Strand 2:   Patterns & Functions

Strand 3:   Algebra

Strand 4:   Geometry

Strand 5:   Measurement

Strand 6:   Data Analysis

Strand 7:   Probability/Uncertainty

To solve the problems related to each strand, you need to create a plan and use a strategy. Remember, there is often more than one strategy that can be used to solve a math problem. You need to choose the strategy that will best help you to solve each problem.

Strand 1: Numbers & Operations

To answer questions about *Numbers & Operations* you will need to

- Represent and use equivalent forms of numbers
- Compare and order fractions, decimals, and percents
- Use factors, multiples, and prime factorization to solve problems
- Use the associative, commutative, and distributive properties
- Add, subtract, multiply, and divide to solve problems
- Compare numbers and make estimates

Directions: Questions 1-8 are all about *Numbers & Operations*. Create a plan and choose a strategy to solve each of these problems.

Modeled Instruction

1 Look at the number sentence below.

$$7^2 \cdot 4 \div (2^3 + 24 \div 4) - 3 \cdot 4 = \underline{\qquad}$$

Which of the following should you perform first in order to solve this problem correctly?

Ⓐ 7^2 Ⓑ 2^3 Ⓒ $24 \div 4$ Ⓓ $3 \cdot 4$

DECIDE what you are being asked to do.

The number sentence given in the problem contains several mathematical operations. You must identify which operation should be performed first in order to solve the problem correctly.

FIND what you need to know.

You are given a number sentence:

$$7^2 \cdot 4 \div (2^3 + 24 \div 4) - 3 \cdot 4 = \underline{\qquad}$$

CHOOSE a strategy for solving the problem.

In order to know which operation should be performed first, you must apply the correct order of operations. *Use a Formula or Rule* is the best strategy for solving this problem.

SOLVE the problem.

List each step of the rule for the order of operations.

Step 1: Perform operations inside parentheses.

Step 2: Simplify all exponents from left to right.

Step 3: Multiply and divide from left to right.

Step 4: Add and subtract from left to right.

By applying Step 1 of the rule to the number sentence, you know that the operations inside the parenthesis should be performed first. This narrows the choice of possible answers to the following:

Choice B: 2^3

Choice C: $24 \div 4$

By applying Steps 2 and 3 of the rule to the number sentence, you know that exponents should be simplified before you divide. Therefore, choice "B" is the correct answer.

CHECK your answer.

Carefully review the rule for order of operations. Solve the entire problem using the rule. Take note of each operation that you perform as you go. Remember to perform operations inside the parenthesis first.

$7^2 \cdot 4 \div (\mathbf{2^3} + 24 \div 4) - 3 \cdot 4 = $ _____ $\longrightarrow$ Simplify exponents inside parenthesis.

$7^2 \cdot 4 \div (8 + \mathbf{24 \div 4}) - 3 \cdot 4 = $ _____ $\longrightarrow$ Divide from left to right inside parenthesis.

$7^2 \cdot 4 \div (\mathbf{8 + 6}) - 3 \cdot 4 = $ _____ $\longrightarrow$ Add from left to right inside parenthesis.

$\mathbf{7^2} \cdot 4 \div (14) - 3 \cdot 4 = $ _____ $\longrightarrow$ Simplify exponents.

$\mathbf{49 \cdot 4} \div (14) - \mathbf{3 \cdot 4} = $ _____ $\longrightarrow$ Multiply from left to right.

$\mathbf{196 \div (14)} - 12 = $ _____ $\longrightarrow$ Divide from left to right.

$\mathbf{14 - 12} = 2 \longrightarrow$ Subtract from left to right.

Compare these steps to each answer choice. Does your answer make sense?

Guided Instruction

2 Look at the numbers below.

67% $\frac{2}{3}$ .6695 $\frac{13}{20}$

Which of these numbers is greatest in value?

Ⓐ 67%   Ⓑ $\frac{2}{3}$ Ⓒ .6695   Ⓓ $\frac{13}{20}$

Hint: *Organize— Make a Chart or List.* Convert all of the numbers listed to decimals and arrange in order from greatest to least.

---

3 There are 840 students at Greenfield Middle School. The graph below shows what portion of students prefers milk, water, and juice with their lunch.

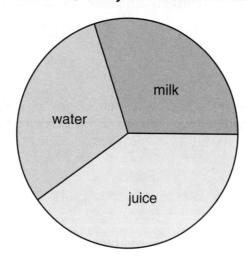

Hint: *Make Estimates.* Look at the graph and estimate what percentage of students prefers milk and water. Use that percentage to calculate how many students prefer juice.

About how many students prefer to drink juice with their lunch?

Ⓐ 200   Ⓑ 300   Ⓒ 400   Ⓓ 500

---

4 Inga walks at a pace of 1.2 miles in 20 minutes. At this pace, how many miles will Inga walk in 1.25 hours?

Answer:_____

Hint: *Compute—Write a Number Sentence, Use a Ratio or Proportion.* Write a proportion that represents the relationship between miles walked and the number of minutes it took.

Independent Study

5 **Which of the following represents the prime factorization for the number 2,601?**

Ⓐ 51^2

Ⓑ $3^3 \cdot 17^2$

Ⓒ $3^2 \cdot 17^2$

Ⓓ $3 \cdot 17 \cdot 51$

 What strategy did you use to solve this problem? _____

_____

6 **Which set of numbers is greater than $\sqrt{64}$ and less than 4^3?**

Ⓐ 9, 19, 11, 45, 36, 64, 53

Ⓑ 20, 8, 63, 47, 9, 56, 44

Ⓒ 12, 21, 35, 64, 40, 53, 8

Ⓓ 39, 9, 63, 13, 25, 51, 42

 What strategy did you use to solve this problem? _____

_____

7 **The table below shows how many jellybeans of each color are in a jar.**

Color of Jellybean	Quantity
Red	42
Green	27
Yellow	39
White	19
Black	23

What percentage of the jellybeans is yellow?

Answer: _____

 What strategy did you use to solve this problem? _____

_____

8 Diego must use 2.4 pounds of flour to make enough dough for 8 slices of pizza. Diego needs to know exactly how many pounds of flour to use in order to make 25 slices of pizza. Explain the steps he should take to calculate the amount of flour he will need.

Answer:

Write a mathematical expression that can be used to calculate how many pounds of flour Diego should use to make 25 slices of pizza.

Answer: _____

 What strategy did you use to solve this problem? _____
_____

Strand 2: Patterns & Functions

To answer questions about *Patterns & Functions* you will need to

• Analyze and represent patterns using rules
• Sort, classify, and order objects
• Continue patterns that repeat or grow
• Identify relationships between objects and numbers

Directions: Questions 1-8 are all about *Patterns & Functions*. Create a plan and choose a strategy to solve each of these problems.

Modeled Instruction

1 **Look at the number pattern below.**

120,000   24,000   4,800   960   192   38.4   7.68   _____?_____

What is the next number in this pattern?

Answer:_____

DECIDE what you are being asked to do.

You must find the next number in the pattern. To do this, you must first determine what the pattern is.

FIND what you need to know.

You know that each number in the pattern is less than the previous number.

CHOOSE a strategy for solving the problem.

To solve the problem, you will need to identify the mathematical operation, or series of operations, that created this pattern. Very large numbers and decimals are easier to work with if they are simplified. *Make It Simpler* is a good strategy for solving this problem.

SOLVE the problem.

Start by looking at just a few numbers in the pattern rather than the whole thing.

Simplify the first three numbers in this pattern by removing an equal number of zeros from each.

120,0~~00~~	$\longrightarrow$	1,200
24,0~~00~~	$\longrightarrow$	240
4,8~~00~~	$\longrightarrow$	48

Consider how the value of each number has changed from the number before it. Each number is less than the previous number. Since division and subtraction are used to reduce the value of a number, try using either of these mathematical operations to find the pattern.

If you use division, you will find that each number in the pattern is divided by 5 to arrive at the next number in the pattern.

$$1{,}200 \div 5 = 240$$
$$240 \div 5 = 48$$

Using this information, extend the pattern by dividing the last number by 5.

$$5\overline{)7.68} = 1.536$$

This calculation shows that the next number in the pattern is 1.536.

CHECK your answer.

Check your answer by applying the rule "divide by 5" to the entire pattern. Make sure that each number in the pattern, when divided by 5, is equal to the next number in the pattern.

120,000 ÷ 5 = 24,000 ÷ 5 = 4,800 ÷ 5 = 960 ÷ 5 = 192 ÷ 5 = 38.4 ÷ 5 = 7.68 ÷ 5 = 1.536

You can also multiply by 5 and work backwards to check the pattern.

1.536 · 5 = 7.68 · 5 = 38.4 · 5 = 192 · 5 = 960 · 5 = 4,800 · 5 = 24,000 · 5 = 120,000

Guided Instruction

2 Veronica raised money for charity by jogging after school each day last week. The amount of money she raised each day is based upon how many miles she jogged. The table below shows how many miles she jogged each day and how much money she raised.

Day	Miles Jogged	Money Raised
Monday	$3\frac{1}{8}$ mi	$57.00
Tuesday	$2\frac{1}{2}$ mi	$45.60
Wednesday	$4\frac{1}{4}$ mi	$77.52
Thursday	$3\frac{5}{8}$ mi	$66.12
Friday	$2\frac{3}{4}$ mi	?

Hint: *Compute—Write a Number Sentence, Use a Ratio or Proportion.* Write a number sentence to calculate how much money Veronica raises for each mile that she jogs. Use this information to find how much money Veronica will raise if she jogs 2 miles.

How much money did Veronica raise on Friday?

(A) $52.25   (B) $50.16   (C) $49.62   (D) $47.50

---

3 Look at the group of numbers inside the box below. Only certain numbers can belong to this group.

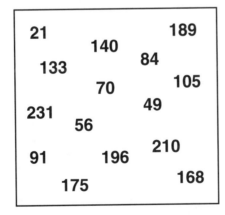

Hint: *Use a Formula or Rule.* Ask yourself what all of the numbers in the box might have in common. Create a rule, and look for the answer choice with a set of numbers that follows the same rule.

Which of the following sets of numbers could also be placed inside the box?

(A)   33, 98, 150, 182, 204

(B)   26, 63, 119, 145, 200

(C)   35, 77, 112, 154, 203

(D)   28, 55, 126, 183, 201

4 **The telephone numbers in a phone book follow the pattern below.**

325-1010	**417-1212**	**515-1111**
335-1111	**449-1717**	**537-1515**
365-1414	**487-1919**	**546-1515**
361-1010	**438-1515**	**581-1414**
364-1313	**444-1212**	**558-1818**

What would be the last four digits of a phone number that begins with "633"?

Answer: _____

Hint: *Look for a Pattern.*
Look closely at the telephone numbers listed. Try adding the first three digits of each number. Do you see a relationship between the last four digits and the sum of the first three digits?

LEVEL G

5 Kasia sorts some numbers into columns as shown below.

A	B	C	D
121	119	115	114
143	133	140	126
176	154	155	150
187	182	170	183

In which column should the number 153 be placed?

Ⓐ   Column A

Ⓑ   Column B

Ⓒ   Column C

Ⓓ   Column D

 What strategy did you use to solve this problem? _____

_____

6 On Monday, Audrey places 1 red marble and 2 blue marbles inside an empty jar. On Tuesday, she adds 2 red marbles and 4 blue marbles to the jar. On Wednesday, Thursday, and Friday Audrey continues to add 1 more red marble than the day before and 2 times as many blue marbles as the day before. How many marbles in all will be in the jar by the end of the day on Friday?

Ⓐ   98

Ⓑ   77

Ⓒ   40

Ⓓ   25

 What strategy did you use to solve this problem? _____

_____

7 Study the number grids below. The last grid is missing a number.

1	9	7
5	42	4
6	8	2

2	7	5
3	38	9
5	6	1

2	4	1
5	29	7
6	1	3

8	1	5
9	43	7
3	8	2

9	2	5
3	?	7
4	1	6

What number is missing from the last grid?

Answer: _____

What strategy did you use to solve this problem? _____

_____

8 A factory packed some school supplies into large crates. The table below shows how many pencils, crayons, and pens are packed together inside a certain number of crates.

Number of Crates	23	28	33	38
Number of Pencils	5,750	7,000	8,250	9,500
Number of Crayons	7,475	9,100	10,725	12,350
Number of Pens	4,025	4,900	5,775	6,650

If the factory packed 16,575 crayons in a certain number of crates, how many pencils did it pack in the same number of crates?

Answer: _____

 What strategy did you use to solve this problem? _____

_____

LEVEL G

Strand 3: Algebra

To answer questions about *Algebra* you will need to

- Represent and analyze mathematical situations using algebraic symbols
- Express mathematical relationships using equations
- Identify how change in one variable relates to change in another variable
- Identify and describe rate of change

Directions: Questions 1-8 are all about *Algebra*. Create a plan and choose a strategy to solve each of these problems.

Modeled Instruction

1   **Look at the equation below.**

$$3(x + 8) = y$$

Which of the following values for *x* and *y* correctly complete the equation?

Ⓐ $x = 13$ and $y = 47$

Ⓑ $x = 14$ and $y = 62$

Ⓒ $x = 15$ and $y = 53$

Ⓓ $x = 16$ and $y = 72$

DECIDE what you are being asked to do.

You must find the values for *x* and *y* that will correctly complete the equation.

FIND what you need to know.

The equation shown will help you find the answer. You know that numbers can be substituted for both *x* and *y*. The number that can be substituted for *x* should be added to 8 and then multiplied by 3 to equal the number that can be substituted for *y*.

CHOOSE a strategy for solving the problem.

The values for x and y that will complete the equation correctly can be found in one of the answer choices. One strategy for solving this type of problem is to *Guess and Check*.

SOLVE the problem.

Substitute the values for x and y from each answer choice into the equation. Only one answer choice can complete the equation correctly.

Choice A: $3(13 + 8) \neq 47$, therefore choice "A" is NOT correct.

Choice B: $3(14 + 8) \neq 62$, therefore choice "B" is NOT correct.

Choice C: $3(15 + 8) \neq 53$, therefore choice "C" is NOT correct.

Choice D: $3(16 + 8) = 72$, therefore choice "D" is the correct answer.

CHECK your answer.

Did you replace x and y in the equation with the correct numbers from the answer choices? Check that you added and multiplied correctly. Ask yourself if your answer makes sense.

Guided Instruction

2 Kayla, Emma, and Chi each have the same number of coins in all. Kayla has 11 quarters, 16 dimes, and 9 pennies. Chi has 4 more quarters than Kayla and 19 dimes. Emma has 2 fewer quarters than Kayla and 5 more dimes than Chi. Both Emma and Chi also have some pennies. How many pennies does Chi have?

   Ⓐ 2   Ⓒ 4

   Ⓑ 3   Ⓓ 5

Hint: *Organize— Make a Chart or List, Graph, Sort Data.* Make a chart to show how many of each coin Kayla, Emma, and Chi has. Use the clues in the problem to find any information missing from the chart you make.

---

3 The students in Mr. Ortega's class will wash some cars to raise money for their school. Their goal is to wash a total of 17 cars. For every 5 cars that they wash, the students will use 21.25 gallons of water and 32.50 ounces of cleaning solution. How many gallons of water will be used to wash all 17 cars?

   Ⓐ 53.75   Ⓒ 95.75

   Ⓑ 72.25   Ⓓ 110.50

Hint: *Compute—Write a Number Sentence, Use a Ratio or Proportion.* Create a ratio that shows how many gallons of water are needed to wash five cars. Use this ratio to create a proportion that can be used to calculate how many gallons of water are needed to wash 17 cars.

---

4 Keith's mother gave him some money to buy groceries at the store. Keith paid $2.98 for one loaf of bread. He also purchased 7 apples and 12 oranges. Each apple cost $0.25, and each orange cost $0.15 more than an apple. In addition to bread and fruit, Keith bought some soup. He bought 3 cans of vegetable soup for $1.03 each. He also bought 2 cans of chicken noodle soup. Each one cost $0.37 less than a can of vegetable soup. After Keith purchased all of these groceries, he had $38.56 left from the money his mother gave him. How much money did Keith's mother give him to begin with?

Hint: *Work Backwards.* Use the information in the problem to work backwards from $38.56 to find how much money Keith's mother gave him to begin with.

Answer: _____

Independent Study

5 **Look at the equation below.**

$$19(32 + x) = 1,140$$

Which word problem can be solved using this equation?

(A) A total of 1,140 nails were used to build 19 picnic tables. Of the nails used to build each table, 32 of them measure 2 inches in length. Find x, the number of nails used to build each picnic table that do not measure 2 inches in length.

(B) A factory uses 1,140 nails to build 32 picnic tables. Of the nails that were used, 19 of them measure 2 inches in length. Find x, the total number of nails used that do not measure 2 inches in length.

(C) A grocery store has 19 cash registers. A total of 1,140 customers buy goods at the grocery store in 1 day. Each customer buys more than 32 apples. Find x, the average number of apples that each customer buys in one day.

(D) A grocery store sold 32 apples and 19 oranges to each of its customers. In all, the grocery store sold 1,140 pieces of fruit. Find x, the number of customers that bought fruit at the grocery store.

 What strategy did you use to solve this problem? _____

_____

6 **Suwan and Avery play on the school basketball team. In one game, Suwan scored 22 points and Avery scored 18 points. In the same game, the rest of the team scored as many points as Suwan and Avery combined. About what percentage of the points scored by the entire team were scored by Avery?**

(A) 21%

(B) 23%

(C) 25%

(D) 27%

 What strategy did you use to solve this problem? _____

_____

7 **The ratio of blue buttons to red buttons in a box is 5:8. How many blue buttons are in a box that has 15,000 red buttons?**

Answer: _____

What strategy did you use to solve this problem? _____

_____

8 **The contents of a box weigh exactly 28 pounds. At least one of each of the items shown below is inside the box.**

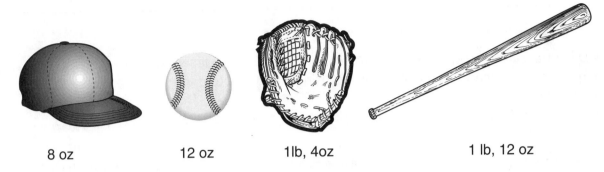

8 oz   12 oz   1lb, 4oz   1 lb, 12 oz

How many of each item might be in the box?

Answer:

 What strategy did you use to solve this problem? _____

_____

To answer questions about *Geometry* you will need to

- Describe, classify, and compare two-dimensional and three-dimensional objects
- Specify and describe spatial relationships using a coordinate grid
- Combine and transform shapes
- Analyze relationships between angles, side lengths, perimeters, areas, and volumes of similar objects

Directions: Questions 1-8 are all about *Geometry*. Create a plan and choose a strategy to solve each of these problems.

Modeled Instruction

1 Look at quadrilateral *QRST* on the coordinate grid to the right.

What would be the coordinates of each vertex if this quadrilateral were translated 4 units to the right and 2 units down?

Answer:

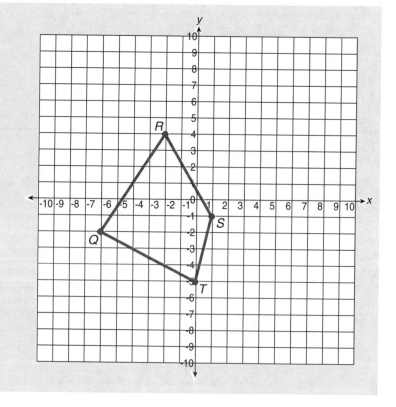

DECIDE what you are being asked to do.

You must determine the coordinates of each vertex when quadrilateral *QRST* is translated 4 units to the right and 2 units down.

FIND what you need to know.

The diagram given in the problem shows where each vertex of quadrilateral *QRST* is located. You must know that each vertex is moved the same number of units in the same direction when a figure is translated to a new location on a coordinate grid.

CHOOSE a strategy for solving the problem.

To solve this problem, you must plot the location of each vertex after the quadrilateral has been translated. *Use Manipulatives or Act Out* is a good strategy for solving this type of problem.

SOLVE the problem.

You can act out the problem by counting the distance that each vertex should be moved on the coordinate grid. Move each vertex 4 units to the right and 2 units down. Plot the new location of each vertex on the coordinate grid.

Write down the coordinates of each new vertex.

Point Q: (⁻2,⁻4)

Point R: (2,2)

Point S: (5,⁻3)

Point T: (4,⁻7)

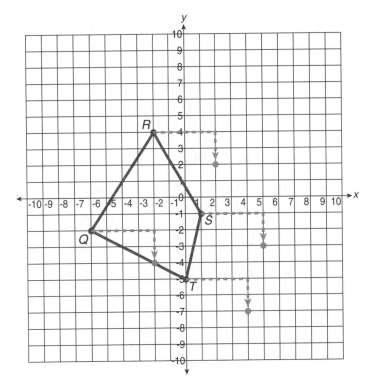

CHECK your answer.

Draw lines to connect each of the vertices you plotted on the coordinate grid, and compare the figure to the original quadrilateral.

When a figure is translated, it remains the same size and shape. Is the new figure the same size and shape as the original? Be sure you translated the figure 4 units to the right and 2 units down.

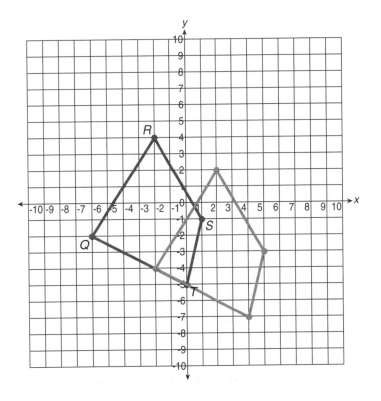

Guided Instruction

2 If ∠E is equal to 63°, and ∠E and ∠F are complementary angles what is the measure of ∠F?

   Ⓐ 27°   Ⓑ 63°   Ⓒ 117°   Ⓓ 126°

Hint: *Use a Formula or Rule.*
Think about what it means for two angles to be complements of each other. Use the rule for complementary angles to answer this question.

---

3 Which of the following describes a triangular prism?

   Ⓐ   It has 5 faces, 8 edges, and 5 vertices.

   Ⓑ   It has 5 faces, 9 edges, and 6 vertices.

   Ⓒ   It has 6 faces, 10 edges, and 8 vertices.

   Ⓓ   It has 6 faces, 12 edges, and 9 vertices.

Hint: *Draw a Picture or Diagram.*
Draw a triangular prism. Count the number of faces, edges, and vertices that it has.

---

4 Diana wants to draw a rhombus on the coordinate grid below. So far, she has plotted three of the vertices.

Hint: *Use Manipulatives or Act Out.*
Look at the location of each vertex shown on the coordinate grid. Count along the x and y axes to locate where the last vertex should be positioned to form a rhombus.

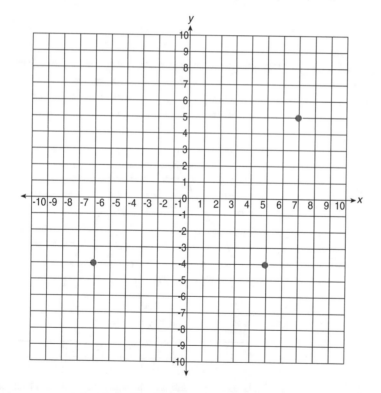

At what coordinates should Diana plot the last vertex of the rhombus?

Answer: _____

5 In the illustration below, ∠*DEF* is a straight angle.

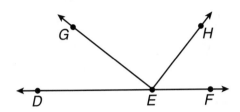

Which angles are supplementary?

Ⓐ   ∠*DEG* and ∠*GEH*

Ⓑ   ∠*DEH* and ∠*HEF*

Ⓒ   ∠*GEH* and ∠*HEF*

Ⓓ   ∠*GEF* and ∠*GEH*

 What strategy did you use to solve this problem? _____

_____

6 Triangle *GHI* is similar to triangle *GEF.*

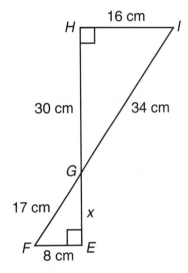

Which proportion can be used to calculate the value of *x*?

Ⓐ $\dfrac{17}{34} = \dfrac{x}{8}$

Ⓑ $\dfrac{30}{34} = \dfrac{17}{x}$

Ⓒ $\dfrac{8}{16} = \dfrac{x}{16}$

Ⓓ $\dfrac{16}{30} = \dfrac{8}{x}$

 What strategy did you use to solve this problem? _____

_____

7 The net below can be folded to form a solid figure.

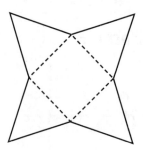

What solid figure can be formed from this net?

Answer: _____

  What strategy did you use to solve this problem? _____

_____

---

8 Draw a reflection of parallelogram *WXYZ* on the coordinate grid below.

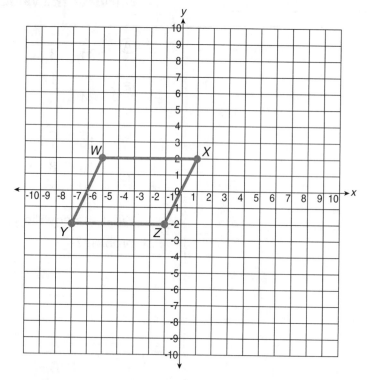

What are the coordinates for the vertices of the reflection you have drawn?

Answer:

  What strategy did you use to solve this problem? _____

_____

Strand 5: Measurement

To answer questions about *Measurement* you will need to

- Measure length, area, perimeter, and volume
- Measure capacity, weight, temperature, and time
- Measure angles
- Convert measurements
- Understand and use both metric and customary systems of measurement
- Use tools to measure attributes of an object

Directions: Questions 1-8 are all about *Measurement*. Create a plan and choose a strategy to solve each of these problems.

Modeled Instruction

1   There were 3 gallons of fruit juice in a large punch bowl. Some students drank 12 pints of fruit juice. Then, 5 quarts of juice were added to the punch bowl. How much juice is in the bowl now?

    Ⓐ   13 quarts   Ⓒ   11 quarts

    Ⓑ   12 quarts   Ⓓ   10 quarts

DECIDE what you are being asked to do.

You must calculate how much fruit juice is in the punch bowl after the students drank some and more was added.

FIND what you need to know.

You can find the following information in the problem:

- Amount of fruit juice in the punch bowl to begin with = 3 gallons

- Amount of fruit juice the students drank = 12 pints

- Amount of fruit juice added to the bowl after the students drank some = 5 quarts

CHOOSE a strategy for solving the problem.

Several units of measurement are used in this problem–gallons, pints and quarts. It would be easier to calculate how much fruit juice is in the punch bowl if you used one common unit of measurement. A good strategy for solving this problem is to *Make It Simpler.*

SOLVE the problem.

Since quarts is the unit of measurement stated in all of the answer choices, convert all the measurements in the problem into quarts.

First, determine how many quarts of fruit juice were in the punch bowl to begin with.

There are 4 quarts in 1 gallon. ⟶ 3 gallons = 12 quarts

Next, determine how many quarts of fruit juice the students drank.

There are 2 pints in 1 quart. ⟶ 12 pints = 6 quarts

The amount of fruit juice added back into the punch bowl is already given as 5 quarts, so you do not need to convert this measurement.

Now that you have simplified this problem, you can calculate the correct answer by writing a number sentence.

amount of juice in the bowl to begin with		amount of juice the students drank		amount of juice added back into the bowl		amount of juice now in the bowl
12 quarts	−	6 quarts	+	5 quarts	=	11 quarts

These calculations show that there are 11 quarts of fruit juice now in the punch bowl. Therefore, choice "C" is the correct answer.

CHECK your answer.

Carefully check that you have converted all measurements in the problem correctly. Be sure that your number sentence shows how much juice is now in the bowl. Check your addition and subtraction.

Guided Instruction

2 **The diameter of a round swimming pool is 6 meters. Its depth is 1.5 meters. What is the approximate circumference of the pool?**

Ⓐ 12 meters

Ⓒ 17 meters

Ⓑ 14 meters

Ⓓ 19 meters

Hint: *Make Estimates.* In order to calculate the circumference of a circle, you must multiply the diameter by π. You can use 3.14 as an estimate for the value of π.

---

3 **Some cube-shaped boxes are stacked on a pallet at a warehouse. Each box measures 24 inches in height. A total of 27 boxes are stacked on 1 pallet. What is the total volume of one pallet of boxes?**

Ⓐ 108 ft^3

Ⓒ 576 in.^3

Ⓑ 216 ft^3

Ⓓ 648 in.^3

Hint: *Draw a Picture or Diagram.* Draw a diagram to show how the boxes could be stacked on the pallet. Then use the height of each box to calculate the volume of the entire pallet of boxes.

---

4 **The figure below is a trapezoid.**

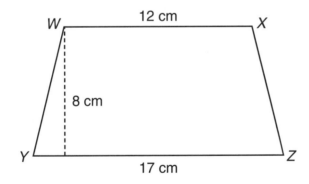

What is the area of this figure?

Answer: _____

Hint: *Use a Formula or Rule.* To solve this problem, use the formula $A = \frac{1}{2}(b_1 + b_2)h$ to calculate the area of a trapezoid.

Independent Study

5 **The top of a picnic table is shaped like a rectangle. The length of the table is equal to 7 feet and its area is equal to 28 square feet. What is the perimeter of the top of the picnic table?**

Ⓐ   35 feet

Ⓑ   22 feet

Ⓒ   14 feet

Ⓓ   11 feet

 What strategy did you use to solve this problem? _____

_____

6 **A truck is hauling 2.25 tons of freight. At a warehouse, 750 pounds of freight are removed from the truck. How much freight is left on the truck?**

Ⓐ   1,500 pounds

Ⓑ   2,250 pounds

Ⓒ   3,750 pounds

Ⓓ   4,500 pounds

 What strategy did you use to solve this problem? _____

_____

7 **A swimming pool filter cleans 3.5 gallons of water in 1 second. How many minutes will it take for the filter to clean 1,680 gallons of water?**

Answer: _____

What strategy did you use to solve this problem? _____

_____

8 **Two boxes have the same volume. One of the boxes is shown below.**

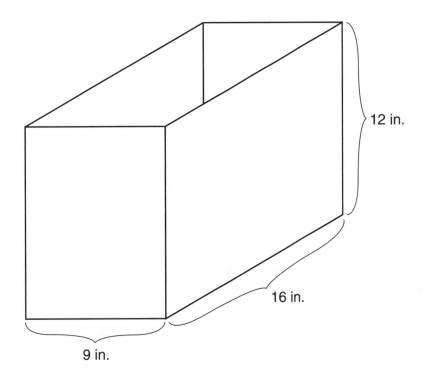

12 in.

16 in.

9 in.

The height of the other box is equal to 8 inches. What are the measurements for the length and width of the other box?

Answer:_____

Explain the steps you took to get your answer.

 What strategy did you use to solve this problem? _____

_____

To answer questions about *Data Analysis* you will need to

• Compare and evaluate data presented in tables and graphs
• Organize and display data into tables and graphs
• Make predictions based on data

Directions: Questions 1-8 are all about *Data Analysis*. Create a plan and choose a strategy to solve each of these problems.

Modeled Instruction

1 The graph below shows how many people attended a concert in each of five different cities.

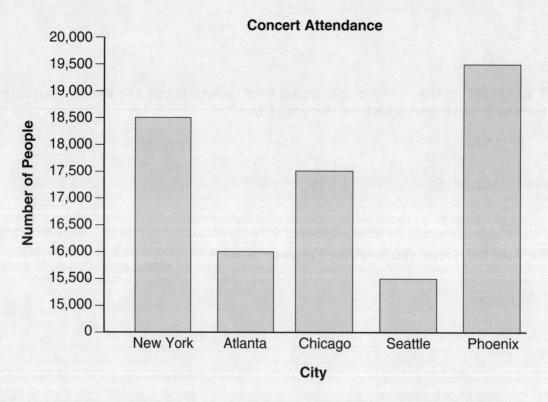

What is the mean attendance for the concert as shown by the data in the graph?

(A) 17,200   (B) 17,300   (C) 17,400   (D) 17,500

DECIDE what you are being asked to do.

You must find the mean of the data set that is shown on the bar graph.

FIND what you need to know.

The bar graph shows how many people attended a concert in each of five cities.

    New York = 18,500

    Atlanta = 16,000

    Chicago = 17,500

    Seattle = 15,500

    Phoenix = 19,500

CHOOSE a strategy for solving the problem.

The mean of a data set is the average of all the numbers in the set. A good strategy for solving this problem is to *Compute—Write a Number Sentence, Use Ratio or Proportion.*

SOLVE the problem.

To find the mean of a data set, add each of the values in the set and then divide by the number of values.

$$\frac{(18,500 + 16,000 + 17,500 + 15,500 + 19,500)}{5} = \frac{87,000}{5} = 17,400$$

The mean of this data set is 17,400. Therefore, choice "C" is the correct answer to this problem.

CHECK your answer.

Look carefully at the height of each bar on the graph, and make sure that you have used the correct data in your number sentence. Check that you have added and divided correctly.

Guided Instruction

2 **Jenny read an entire book in five days. The graph below shows what portion of the book she read each day.**

Portion of Book Read Each Day

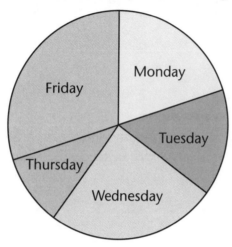

Hint: *Make Estimates.* Use the graph to estimate what percentage of the total number of pages in the book Jenny read each day. Then calculate about how many pages she read on Monday.

If there are a total of 155 pages in the book, about how many pages did Jenny read on Monday?

Ⓐ 10   Ⓒ 30

Ⓑ 20   Ⓓ 40

---

3 **Silvia likes to go bowling. The table to the right shows her score for each of the first five games that she bowled on Saturday.**

	Score
Game 1	121
Game 2	105
Game 3	107
Game 4	132
Game 5	112

Hint: *Compute—Write a Number Sentence, Use a Ratio or Proportion.* Write a number sentence to calculate the total score divided by the total number of games that would equal 115. Use *x* to represent the score that Silvia needs to have in Game 6.

If Silvia were to bowl one more game, what score would she need to have in Game 6 to have a mean score of 115?

Answer: _____

4 **Miguel measured the temperature in three different locations in his backyard throughout the day. He used the data he collected to create the graph below.**

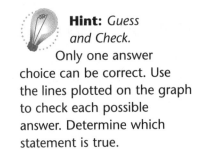

Hint: *Guess and Check.*
Only one answer choice can be correct. Use the lines plotted on the graph to check each possible answer. Determine which statement is true.

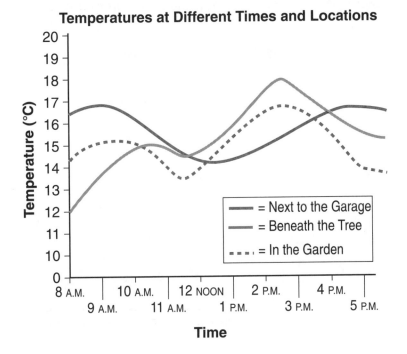

Temperatures at Different Times and Locations

Based on the data in the graph, which of the following statements is true?

Ⓐ At 9:00 A.M., the temperature beneath the tree is greater than the temperature next to the garage and in the garden.

Ⓑ At 11:00 A.M., the temperature beneath the tree is greater than the temperature next to the garage, but less than the temperature in the garden.

Ⓒ At 1:00 P.M., the temperature in the garden is greater than the temperature next to the garage and beneath the tree.

Ⓓ At 3:00 P.M., the temperature in the garden is greater than the temperature next to the garage, but less than the temperature beneath the tree.

Independent Study

The people in six districts voted for the candidate of their choice to become mayor. The graph below shows how many votes each candidate received in each district. Use this graph to answer questions 5-7.

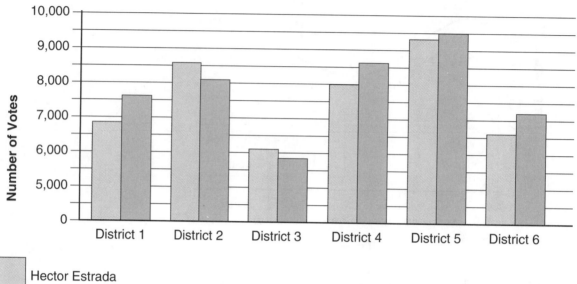

Votes Received by Candidate in Each District

Hector Estrada

Elizabeth Meyers

---

5 **In which district was the range of votes received by both candidates the greatest?**

Ⓐ District 1   Ⓒ District 4

Ⓑ District 2   Ⓓ District 6

 What strategy did you use to solve this problem? _____

_____

6 **About how many votes in all did Elizabeth Meyers receive?**

Ⓐ 55,000   Ⓒ 47,000

Ⓑ 51,000   Ⓓ 44,000

What strategy did you use to solve this problem? _____

_____

---

7 **Which candidate received more votes in all?**

Answer:_____

 What strategy did you use to solve this problem? _____

_____

8 Isabel planted a banana tree and a coconut tree in her backyard. The table below shows the height of each tree at the end of each month for an entire year.

Month	Banana Tree Height (in inches)	Coconut Tree Height (in inches)
January	7	6
February	23	19
March	32	28
April	41	35
May	51	44
June	59	56
July	68	64
August	75	70
September	83	77
October	91	85
November	98	93
December	107	99

Use the information from the table to create a line graph that shows the rate of growth for each of the trees that Isabel planted in her backyard. Be sure to clearly label your graph and give it a title.

What strategy did you use to solve this problem? _____

_____

To answer questions about *Probability/Uncertainty* you will need to

- Measure the likelihood of an event
- Predict the outcomes of simple experiments
- Make inferences based on data
- Use tree diagrams, lists, and models to compute the probability of simple compound events

Directions: Questions 1-8 are all about *Probability/Uncertainty*. Create a plan and choose a strategy to solve each of these problems.

Modeled Instruction

1   **There are two quarters, five nickels, one dime, and three pennies in a cash register. Jason will remove three coins from the cash register at random. He will remove all three coins at the same time. How many different combinations of coins is it possible for Jason to choose?**

Answer: _____

 DECIDE what you are being asked to do.

You must determine how many different outcomes are possible if Jason removes three coins from the cash register at random.

 FIND what you need to know.

You know how many of each coin is in the register:

2 quarters

5 nickels

1 dime

3 pennies

You also know that Jason will remove a total of three coins from the cash register at random and that he will remove them at the same time.

CHOOSE a strategy for solving the problem.

There are several possible outcomes if three coins are removed from the cash register at random. One strategy for identifying all possible outcomes is to *Organize—Make a Chart or List, Graph, Sort Data.*

SOLVE the problem.

To find all of the possible outcomes, make a chart. Write the letter "Q" for quarter, "N" for nickel, "D" for dime, and "P" for penny. Keep in mind that the order in which the coins are listed does not matter, since all three coins will be removed from the cash register at random.

You can see from looking at the chart that there are 15 possible outcomes when 3 coins are removed from the cash register at random.

Possible Outcomes		
Q	Q	N
Q	Q	D
Q	Q	P
Q	N	N
Q	P	P
Q	N	D
Q	N	P
Q	D	P
N	N	N
N	N	D
N	N	P
N	D	P
N	P	P
D	P	P
P	P	P

CHECK your answer.

Make sure that you have listed every possible outcome and that no outcome is listed more than once. For example, if you list N-D-P, you do not need to list N-P-D, D-P-N, D-N-P, P-D-N, or P-N-D. These are all the same combination of coins—they are just listed in a different order.

2 There are 39 large buttons and 53 small buttons in a box. The table to the right shows how many of each color button are in the box.

If one button is removed from the box at random, what is probability that it will be a black or blue button?

Color	Quantity
Black	25
Red	11
Blue	19
Yellow	23
White	14

Hint: *Compute—Write a Number Sentence, Use a Ratio or Proportion.* Write a ratio that represents the total number of possible outcomes to the total number of favorable outcomes. You may need to simplify the ratio to find the correct answer.

Ⓐ $\frac{1}{2}$ Ⓑ $\frac{11}{23}$ Ⓒ $\frac{19}{25}$ Ⓓ $\frac{44}{100}$

---

3 The students in Mr. Pierre's class can choose from several lunch combinations. Each student can choose one sandwich, one snack, and one drink.

How many different lunch combinations do the students in Mr. Pierre's class have to choose from?

Lunch Menu

Sandwiches:
Ham and Cheese
Egg Salad
Peanut Butter and Jelly

Snacks:
Bag of Pretzels
Fruit Cup   **Drinks:**
Banana   Water
                Juice
                Milk

Hint: *Organize—Make a Chart or List, Graph, Sort Data.* Make a list or draw a chart to show all of the different lunch combinations that are possible.

Ⓐ 30   Ⓑ 27   Ⓒ 16   Ⓓ 9

---

4 The following number cards are placed on a table.

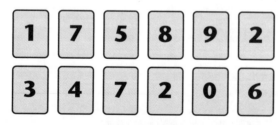

Carol selects two cards at random. She then adds the numbers from both cards. How many possible outcomes will result in a sum of 14?

Hint: *Use Manipulatives or Act Out.* Write the numbers shown on each card onto small pieces of paper. Use these pieces of paper to find as many different combinations as possible that will have a sum of 14.

Answer: _____

Independent Study

5 There are 1,288 marbles inside a large container. If one marble is removed from the container at random, the probability that it will be a blue marble is 11 out of 23. How many blue marbles are inside the container?

- Ⓐ 688
- Ⓑ 635
- Ⓒ 616
- Ⓓ 602

What strategy did you use to solve this problem? _____

_____

6 There are a total of 46 tiles on the floor. Of these tiles, 29 are rectangular in shape and the rest are shaped like a square. Of the tiles that are rectangular in shape, 12 are white and the rest are gray. All of the square-shaped tiles are black. Marleen will pick up one of the tiles from the floor at random. Which of the following statements is true?

- Ⓐ The probability that she will select either a white or black tile is greater than the probability that she will select a rectangular tile.

- Ⓑ The probability that she will select a white tile is the same as the probability that she will select a square tile.

- Ⓒ The probability that she will select either a gray or black tile is less than the probability that she will select a rectangular tile.

- Ⓓ The probability that she will select a gray tile is the same as the probability that she will select a square tile.

What strategy did you use to solve this problem? _____

_____

7 Two number cubes are used to play a game. On each turn, a player rolls both number cubes. Then the player must add the numbers that land face-up to determine how many spaces to move his or her game piece. The numbers on each cube are shown in the table below.

Cube A	1	2	1	1	2	1
Cube B	2	1	3	3	1	2

How many spaces will a player least likely have to move his or her game piece on a turn?

Answer: _____

What strategy did you use to solve this problem? _____

_____

8 Miss Lin keeps her jewelry in a safe. She must enter a four-digit code to open the safe. The code contains each of the following digits.

1   4   7   9

Miss Lin cannot remember the correct order in which she must enter the digits in the code. List all the possible code combinations using the four digits that are shown.

Answer:

What strategy did you use to solve this problem? _____

_____

PART B
Strategies and Strands—
All Together

Section 1:
Problem Solving—
Test A

Section 2:
Problem Solving—
Test B

The problem-solving strategies and math strands are taught all together in this part.

Part B contains two tests. Each test has 35 problems that you will solve on your own. Remember to follow the 5-Step Problem-Solving Plan you learned in Part A. Use the 10 Problem-Solving Strategies. As you master the strategies and strands, you will become a better problem solver and a better test taker.

In each of the tests, there are short-response questions that have an answer grid. Your teacher will tell you whether you should write your answer using this answer grid.

Sample:

John was buying school supplies. He spent $1.50 on a notebook and $0.59 on a pen. How much did he spend all together?

[The answer is $2.09]

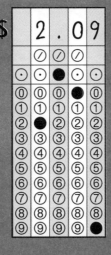

Section 1: Problem Solving—Test A

Directions: Answer questions 1-35. Follow the 5-Step Problem-Solving Plan and choose the best strategy for solving each problem. Be sure to show all of your work. If you need more room, use a separate sheet of paper. Remember to check your answers.

1 Which of the following is the decimal equivalent of the fraction $\frac{7}{8}$?

Ⓐ   .750   Ⓒ   .850

Ⓑ   .785   Ⓓ   .875

2 The chart below shows how much glue is needed to make certain quantities of paper airplanes.

Number of Paper Airplanes	Amount of Glue Needed
13	24.05 oz
21	38.85 oz
29	53.65 oz
37	68.45 oz
45	83.25 oz

How many ounces of glue are needed to make five paper airplanes?

Ⓐ   11.05   Ⓒ   9.25

Ⓑ   10.45   Ⓓ   8.85

3 It snowed in Chicago and in Boston on the same day. In Chicago, it snowed at a rate of 1.3 inches per hour. In Boston, it snowed at a rate of 1.7 inches per hour. Which expression can be used to calculate how many more inches of snow fell in Boston than in Chicago if it snowed for x hours in both cities?

Ⓐ $x(1.7 - 1.3)$ Ⓒ $1.7x - 1.3$

Ⓑ $\dfrac{1.7 - 1.3}{x}$ Ⓓ $1.7 - 1.3x$

4 In the diagram below, $\angle ABC$ is a straight angle and $\angle DBE$ is a right angle.

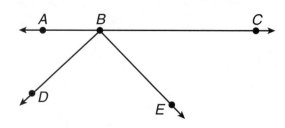

Which angles are supplementary?

Ⓐ $\angle ABD$ and $\angle DBE$

Ⓑ $\angle DBE$ and $\angle EBC$

Ⓒ $\angle ABE$ and $\angle DBC$

Ⓓ $\angle EBC$ and $\angle ABE$

5 Tasha would like to build a circular fence around her vegetable garden. The diameter of the garden measures 7 meters.

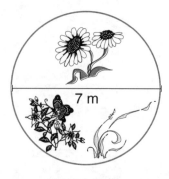

7 m

What is the best estimate for the total length of fence that Tasha will need?

Ⓐ   20 meters   Ⓒ   70 meters

Ⓑ   40 meters   Ⓓ   150 meters

6 The table to the right shows how many of each type of flower were planted in a garden.

Which graph correctly displays the information from the table?

Type of Flower	Quantity
Roses	52
Violets	37
Tulips	18
Daisies	93

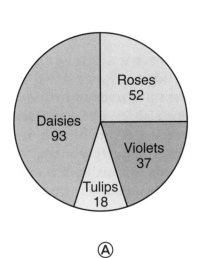

Ⓐ

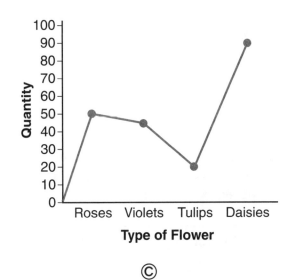

Ⓒ

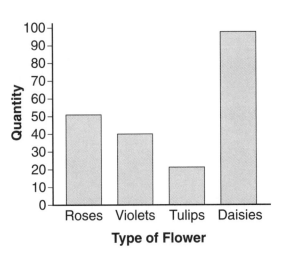

Ⓑ

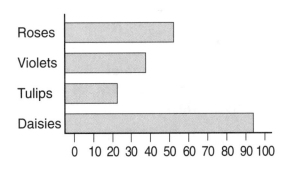

Ⓓ

7 A jar contains 128 pennies, 99 nickels, 102 dimes, and 23 quarters. If one coin is removed from the jar at random, what is the probability that the coin will NOT be a penny?

(A) $\dfrac{1}{128}$

(C) $\dfrac{3}{4}$

(B) $\dfrac{3}{352}$

(D) $\dfrac{7}{11}$

---

8 The table below shows how many students are in each teacher's class at Walker Middle School.

Teacher	Number of Students
Mr. O'Brien	29
Mrs. Vasquez	31
Miss Chue	28
Mr. Parks	32
Mrs. Abbot	25
Mr. Chavez	30

What percentage of the students at Walker Middle School are in Miss Chue's class?

Answer: _____

9 Look at the letter pattern below.

Z, X, Y, W, X, V, W, U, V, T, U, ___ , ___ , ___

What are the next three letters in this pattern?

Answer: _____

---

10 There are a total of 5 blue rubber bands for every 4 red rubber bands that are packed inside a bag. There are also 2 yellow rubber bands for every 1 red rubber band inside the same bag. How many yellow rubber bands are inside a bag that contains 135 blue rubber bands?

Answer: _____

11 Look at quadrilateral *QRST* on the coordinate grid below.

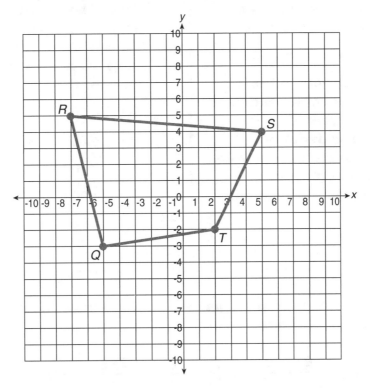

What are the coordinates of each vertex for quadrilateral *QRST*?

Answer:

---

12 The sandbox shown below is shaped like a rectangular prism.

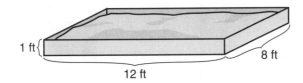

1 ft
12 ft
8 ft

If 2 cubic feet of sand weigh 22.5 pounds, how many pounds of sand are needed to fill the sandbox?

Answer: _____

13 Valerie collected some data about birds in her backyard. She recorded the average temperature each week and the number of birds she observed in her yard during that week. The table below shows the data she collected.

	Average Temperature	Number of Birds
Week 1	77°F	79
Week 2	79°F	77
Week 3	83°F	73
Week 4	86°F	72
Week 5	89°F	69
Week 6	91°F	66

Based on the data in this table, what can you conclude will happen if the temperature continues to increase?

Answer:_____

14 There are a total of 24 crayons in a box. An equal number of crayons are blue and red. The number of yellow crayons is equal to $\frac{1}{8}$ the total number of crayons in the box. There are 6 green crayons, and there are 2 more red crayons than yellow crayons. The remainder of the crayons in the box are orange. What color crayon is least likely to be selected from the box at random?

Answer: _____

15 There are a total of 6,932 fish in a lake. About 45% of the fish in the lake are less than 12 inches in length. What is the best estimate for how many fish in the lake are greater than 12 inches in length?

Ⓐ   4,500

Ⓑ   4,000

Ⓒ   3,500

Ⓓ   3,000

16 Jan is arranging some tiles in the pattern shown below. She must add six more tiles to complete the pattern.

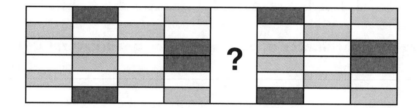

Which series of tiles will complete the pattern correctly?

Ⓐ   Ⓑ    Ⓒ 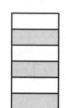   Ⓓ

17 Ethan purchases four notebooks. Each notebook costs $3.25. When Ethan purchases the notebooks, he also pays an additional 7% tax on the total cost of all four notebooks. Ethan gives the cashier $20.00. How much change should the cashier give Ethan?

Ⓐ $9.65

Ⓑ $8.91

Ⓒ $7.75

Ⓓ $6.09

18 Triangle *DEF* is similar to triangle *GHF*.

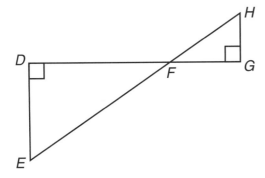

Which line segment corresponds to segment *DF*?

Ⓐ   DE   Ⓒ   GF

Ⓑ   EF   Ⓓ   HF

19 Isha is conducting an experiment. She must record the temperature of a liquid over time as it is heated by a flame. She determines that the temperature of the liquid increases at a rate of .75°C every 5 seconds. Which expression can be used to calculate how much the temperature of the liquid will increase in 2 minutes?

Ⓐ $(.75 \div 5) \times 2$

Ⓑ $\dfrac{.75}{5} \times 120$

Ⓒ $.75 \times 60 \times 2$

Ⓓ $\dfrac{.75}{2} \times 5$

20 Which set of data has a median of 149 and a range of 21?

Ⓐ   142, 146, 158, 151, 137, 149, 155

Ⓑ   149, 168, 149, 163, 147, 154, 157

Ⓒ   146, 153, 161, 147, 139, 149, 157

Ⓓ   155, 141, 148, 149, 157, 152, 149

21 Sonya chooses a prize at random from 1 of 4 boxes. There is a different quantity of each prize in each box as shown below

Box A	Box B	Box C	Box D
12 bracelets	18 bracelets	17 bracelets	0 bracelets
15 pens	0 pens	13 pens	18 pens
17 necklaces	14 necklaces	15 necklaces	11 necklaces
19 coins	15 coins	11 coins	0 coins
16 stickers	10 stickers	0 stickers	19 stickers

Sonya has the best chance of choosing a necklace from which box?

Ⓐ   Box A

Ⓑ   Box B

Ⓒ   Box C

Ⓓ   Box D

---

22 Isaac filled nine large cups and seven small cups with juice. Each large cup holds 9.85 ounces of juice, and each small cup holds 6.50 ounces of juice. How many more ounces of juice in all did Isaac pour into the large cups than into the small cups?

Answer: _____

LEVEL G

23 At the beginning of the year, Keisha has $200 in the bank. At the end of every month she takes $25 from the bank to spend. She also puts $75 in the bank every other month. How much money will Keisha have in the bank after 12 months?

Answer: _____

24 Madison is 4 years younger than Emilio. Emilio is twice as old as Wendy and 2 years older than Greg. How old will Greg be when Madison is 19 years old?

Answer: _____

25 The measure of $\angle P$ in a rhombus is equal to 65.25°. What is the measure, in degrees, of the angle that is opposite $\angle P$?

Answer: _____

26 There are 25 containers on a table. Each container holds 1,450 milliliters of water. How many liters of water in all are in the containers that are on the table?

Answer: _____

27 Dora plays on the school basketball team. The list below shows how many points she scored in each game that she has played so far this season.

39, 21, 28, 35, 32, 19, 29, 32

How many points will Dora need to score in the next game that she plays in order to have a mean number of points scored equal to 30?

Answer: _____

28 Some tokens are placed inside a bag. Of the tokens placed in the bag, 144 are blue. The probability of selecting one blue token from the bag at random is 3 out of 8. How many tokens in all are inside the bag?

Answer: _____

29 Olivia likes to collect stamps. She has a total of 945 stamps in her collection. Olivia's father gave her $\frac{1}{3}$ of the stamps in her collection, and Olivia's sister gave her $\frac{2}{7}$ of the stamps. The rest of the stamps in Olivia's collection are from her uncle. What simplified fraction represents the portion of stamps in Olivia's collection that are from her uncle?

Answer: _____

How many stamps did Olivia's uncle give to her?

Answer: _____

30 The chart below shows a pattern for how the population of a town has changed over time.

Year	1994	1996	1998	2000	2002	2004
Population	4,750	5,175	5,575	5,950	6,300	6,625

Describe the pattern for how the town's population has changed.

Answer:

If this pattern continues, what will the town's population be in the year 2010?

Answer: _____

31 **Look at the sequence of numbers below.**

1, 2, 12, 20, 20, 42, 56, ...

Write an expression that can be used to determine the value of the *n*th term in this sequence.

Answer:

Use the expression you've written to find the value of the 12th term in this sequence.

Answer: _____

32 The figure below is a triangular prism.

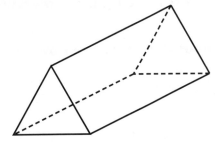

In the space below, draw a net that represents a triangular prism.

How many edges does a triangular prism have?

Answer: _____

33 A square-shaped carpet is placed on the floor. One side of the carpet measures 7.5 feet in length. The floor is rectangular. It measures 18.0 feet in length and 9.5 feet in width.

What is the area of the floor that is covered by the carpet?

Answer: _____

What is the area of the floor that is NOT covered by the carpet?

Answer: _____

34 The table below shows the altitude of an airplane at different time intervals during a flight.

Flight Time (from time of take off)	Altitude (feet above ground)
0 min	0 ft
5 min	15,300 ft
10 min	29,500 ft
15 min	36,700 ft
30 min	41,200 ft
45 min	41,000 ft
60 min	37,600 ft
70 min	24,700 ft
75 min	18,500 ft
80 min	0 ft

Use the data from the table to create a line graph that shows the altitude of the airplane at each time interval. Be sure to clearly label your graph and give it a title.

35 Jamal, Clara, Kim, and Linda are standing in line at the school cafeteria. They are standing one in front of the other. List all of the possible combinations for the order in which the four students might be standing if Jamal is either first or last in line.

Answer:

PART B
Strategies and Strands— *All Together*

Section 2: Problem Solving— Test B

Section 2: Problem Solving—Test B

Directions: Answer questions 1-35. Follow the 5-Step Problem-Solving Plan and choose the best strategy for solving each problem. Be sure to show all of your work. If you need more room, use a separate sheet of paper. Remember to check your answers.

1 Look at the inequality below.

$$-7 < \boxed{} < \sqrt{9}$$

Which integer belongs in the empty box?

- Ⓐ 7
- Ⓑ 4
- Ⓒ ⁻1
- Ⓓ ⁻8

2 The numbers in each column have something in common with each other.

A	B	C	D
48	35	56	27
24	10	84	63
90	95	21	36
18	85	49	99
66	40	91	72

In which column does the number 78 belong?

- Ⓐ Column A
- Ⓑ Column B
- Ⓒ Column C
- Ⓓ Column D

3 Tim answered 27 questions correctly on a math test. Dawn answered four fewer questions correctly than Tim. Owen answered more questions correctly than Dawn, but fewer than Tim. Which inequality expresses how many questions Owen answered correctly?

- Ⓐ $27 - 4 > x > 27$
- Ⓑ $27 > x > 27 - 4$
- Ⓒ $27 + 4 < x < 27$
- Ⓓ $27 < x < 27 + 4$

4 Which of the following statements about an acute triangle is NOT true?

- Ⓐ It is possible for an angle in an acute triangle to measure 60°.
- Ⓑ It is possible for an acute triangle to also be an equilateral triangle.
- Ⓒ The sum of all three angles in an acute triangle must equal 180°.
- Ⓓ All three sides in an acute triangle must be congruent.

5 A circular pool has a diameter of 18.0 feet and measures 4.5 feet in height. About how much water is needed to fill this pool?

(A) 1,418 cubic feet

(B) 1,144 cubic feet

(C) 572 cubic feet

(D) 254 cubic feet

6 A census is being conducted to see how many children live in each household within the city. Which measure of data would best determine how many children live in most households?

(A) range

(B) mean

(C) median

(D) mode

7 A bowl contains 480 jellybeans. The probability of selecting a green jellybean from the bowl at random is 1 out of 5. What portion of the jellybeans in the bowl are green?

(A) 5%

(B) 10%

(C) 15%

(D) 20%

8 Fred paid $21.75 to buy three tickets to see a movie. What mathematical expression could be used to calculate how much it would cost Fred to purchase ten tickets?

Answer: _____

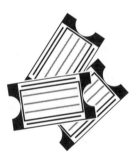

9 The decimals below follow a pattern.

.3	.15	.075		.01875

What decimal is missing from this pattern?

Answer: _____

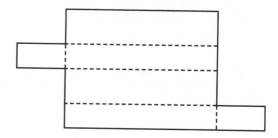

11 The net below can be folded to form a solid figure.

What solid figure can be formed from this net?

Answer: _____

12 A bird that is flying at a constant rate of speed can fly 120 miles in 2 hours. How far can the bird fly in 30 seconds?

Answer: _____

10 The ratio of boys to girls at Sanford Middle School is 8:9. If there are 935 students at Sanford Middle School, how many are boys?

Answer: _____

13 The graph below shows the percentage of children at Lauderville Middle School that chose each type of animal as their favorite pet when asked during a survey.

Favorite Pets

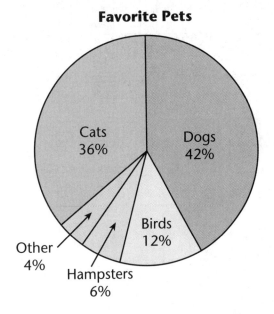

If a total of 650 students participated in the survey, how many more students chose dogs than cats as their favorite pet?

Answer:_____

---

14 Sid must type a four-letter code to log on to his computer. The code that he must type includes the letters E, J, Q, and Z. How many different code combinations are possible using these four letters?

Answer: _____

15 There are 80 paper clips in a small box and 120 paper clips in a large box. Which ratio compares the number of paper clips in a small box to the number of paper clips in a large box?

Ⓐ $\frac{4}{5}$

Ⓑ $\frac{2}{3}$

Ⓒ $\frac{5}{4}$

Ⓓ $\frac{3}{2}$

16 **The shaded portions of the grids below follow a pattern.**

If this pattern were continued, how would the next three grids be shaded?

Ⓐ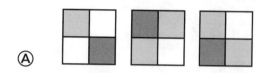

Ⓑ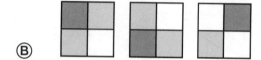

Ⓒ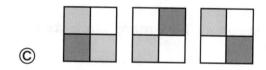

Ⓓ

17 A printing press is used to print newspapers. The printing press can print 3,500 pages in 10 minutes. Each newspaper has 70 pages. How much time will it take to print 850 newspapers?

Ⓐ 2 hours and 50 minutes

Ⓑ 3 hours and 30 minutes

Ⓒ 4 hours and 10 minutes

Ⓓ 5 hours and 20 minutes

18 Point *S* is located at the coordinates (2,6). Point *T* is located 5 units to the left and 7 units down from Point *S*. What are the coordinates of Point *T*?

Ⓐ $(^-7,1)$

Ⓑ $(^-5,1)$

Ⓒ $(^-2,^-1)$

Ⓓ $(^-3,^-1)$

19 The perimeter of a rectangle is equal to 43 centimeters and its area is equal to 105 square centimeters. Which of the following could be the measurements for the length and width of this rectangle?

Ⓐ length = 13 cm and width = 8 cm

Ⓑ length = 15 cm and width = 7 cm

Ⓒ length = 12.5 cm and width = 9 cm

Ⓓ length = 14 cm and width = 7.5 cm

20 The line graph below shows the distance that a car has traveled at different time intervals during a trip from one city to another.

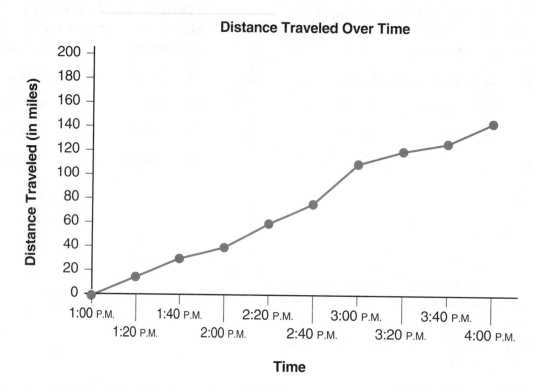

During which period of time did the car travel at the fastest rate of speed?

Ⓐ from 1:20 P.M. to 1:40 P.M.

Ⓑ from 2:00 P.M. to 2:20 P.M.

Ⓒ from 2:40 P.M. to 3:00 P.M.

Ⓓ from 3:20 P.M. to 3:40 P.M.

21 Ann uses 48 cards to play a game. There are numbers on $\frac{2}{3}$ of the cards she uses. There rest of the cards do not have numbers. Of the cards that do have numbers, there are four more cards with odd numbers than with even numbers. If Ann selects one card at random, which of the following is true?

Ⓐ The probability that Ann will select a card with an even number is greater than the probability that she will select a card with an odd number.

Ⓑ The probability that Ann will select a card with an even number is greater than the probability that she will select a card without a number.

Ⓒ The probability that Ann will select a card with an odd number is less than the probability that she will select a card with an even number.

Ⓓ The probability that Ann will select a card with an even number is less than the probability that she will select a card without a number.

22 What is the decimal equivalent of the fraction $\frac{87}{24}$?

Answer: _____

	/	/	/	
⊙	⊙	⊙	⊙	⊙
⓪	⓪	⓪	⓪	⓪
①	①	①	①	①
②	②	②	②	②
③	③	③	③	③
④	④	④	④	④
⑤	⑤	⑤	⑤	⑤
⑥	⑥	⑥	⑥	⑥
⑦	⑦	⑦	⑦	⑦
⑧	⑧	⑧	⑧	⑧
⑨	⑨	⑨	⑨	⑨

23 Sue is on the school track team. The speed at which she can run decreases at a constant rate every 25 meters. The table below shows how much time it takes for her to run certain distances.

Distance	25 m	50 m	75 m	100 m	125 m	150 m
Time	3.5 sec	7.5 sec	12.0 sec	17.0 sec	22.5 sec	28.5 sec

If the rate of speed at which Sue can run continues to decrease as shown in the table, how many seconds will it take for her to run a distance of 200 meters?

Answer: _____

24 The equation below shows a relationship between the value of *x* and the value of *y*.

$$\frac{1}{2}x = y^2$$

What is the value of *x* when *y* is equal to 25?

Answer: _____

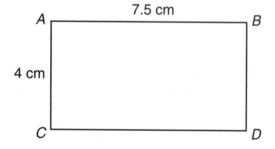

---

25 Rectangle *ABCD* is similar to rectangle *JKLM*.

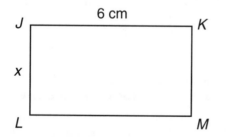

What is the length of side *JL* in centimeters?

Answer: _____

26 Lilly would like to replace some old tiles on her kitchen floor with new tiles. The size and shape of these tiles are shown below.

Old Tile

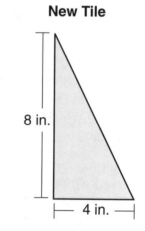

New Tile

How many new tiles are needed to cover the same area as 154 old tiles?

Answer: _____

LEVEL G

27 The table below shows how many inches of rain fell each month during one year in Orlando, Florida.

Jan.	Feb.	Mar.	Apr.	May	June	July	Aug.	Sept.	Oct.	Nov.	Dec.
2.09 in.	4.04 in.	.70 in.	2.28 in.	1.94 in.	12.48 in.	7.29 in.	11.05 in.	6.83 in.	3.12 in.	2.71 in.	10.11 in.

What was the mean rainfall, rounded to the nearest tenth of an inch, for one month during this time period?

Answer: _____

---

28 There are 68 red marbles in a jar. There are 3 fewer blue marbles than red marbles, and there are 7 more green marbles than blue marbles. The rest of the marbles in the jar are yellow. If the probability of selecting one green marble at random is $\frac{3}{11}$, how many marbles are in the jar in all?

Answer: _____

29 Look at the expression below.

$$(25 - 3^2) \div 4 + 9 \cdot 4^3$$

Explain the steps you should take to simplify this expression.

How is this expression written in its simplest form?

Answer: _____

30 The number chart below shows a relationship between the value of *x* and the value of *y*.

x	y
$\frac{1}{4}$	$\frac{1}{2}$
$\frac{1}{3}$	$\frac{2}{3}$
$\frac{3}{8}$	$\frac{3}{4}$
$\frac{2}{5}$	$\frac{4}{5}$

Write a mathematical expression to show the relationship between the value of *x* and the value of *y*.

Answer: _____

If the value of *y* is equal to $\frac{6}{7}$, what is the value of *x* in simplest form?

Answer: _____

31 **Write a word problem that can be solved using the number sentence below.**

$(12 \cdot 9) - (12 \cdot 6) =$ _____

Answer:

Explain the steps you would take to solve the problem you wrote.

32 **A polygon is shown on the coordinate grid below. Draw a reflection of this polygon across the *y*-axis.**

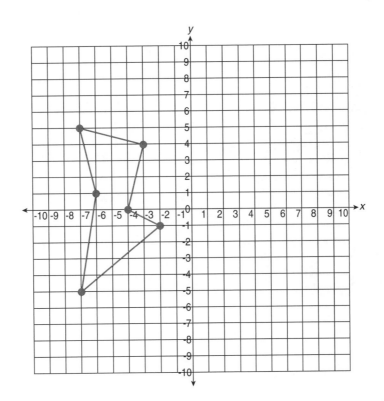

What are the coordinates for each vertex of the polygon that you have drawn?

Answer:_____

33 A box of rice that has a volume equal to 1,200 cubic centimeters can hold 396 grams of rice. What are possible measurements for the length, width, and height of a box that can hold 990 grams of rice?

Answer:

34 Mai, Carlo, and Katie like to read every night before they go to bed. The table below shows how much time Mai, Carlo, and Katie spent reading each night during one week.

Night	Mai	Carlo	Katie
Monday	45 min	1 hr	45 min
Tuesday	20 min	35 min	1 hr
Wednesday	1 hr	50 min	30 min
Thursday	50 min	15 min	1 hr
Friday	40 min	40 min	50 min

Use the information from the table to create a bar graph that shows how much time Mai, Carlo, and Katie spent reading each night during the time period shown. Be sure to clearly label your graph and give it a title.

35 Antonia is shopping for some winter clothes. She would like to buy one hat, one jacket, and one scarf. She can choose from the different colors listed below for each item.

Hats	Jackets	Scarves
Brown	Gray	Black
Yellow	Blue	White
Green		Yellow
		Red

List all of the possible hat, jacket, and scarf color combinations that Antonia can choose from.